New
Sky

1
Activity Book

Jonathan Bygrave
Brian Abbs
Ingrid Freebairn

1 Hello, I'm Rob!

Introduce yourself

1a Complete the conversations.

~~What's~~   I'm   My   name's   what's

Liz   Billy   Peter   Paula

Robogirl

1 **Billy:** Hello! _What's_ your name?
  Paula: I'm Paula.

2 **Robogirl:** Hi! What's your name?
  Liz: Hello! .... Liz.

3 **Liz:** Hi! What's your name?
  Peter: My .... Peter.
  Liz: Hi, Peter!

4 **Peter:** Hello! I'm Peter. What's your name?
  Billy: .... name's Billy.

5 **Paula:** Hi, ... your name?
  Robogirl: I'm Robogirl.

1b Complete the conversations.

Ann: Hello. What's [1] _your name?_ ....

Bob: My [2] ....

Ann: Hi, Bob. I [3] ....

Bob: Hi, [4] ....

Alex: Hi! I'm [5] ....
        [6] .... ?

Betty: My [7] ....

Alex: Hello, [8] ....

he/she

2 Circle the correct words.

1 **A:** Who's *he* / *she* ?
  B: *He's* / *She's* my sister.

2 **A:** Who's *he* / *she*?
  B: *He's* / *She's* my brother.

3 **A:** Who's Dan?
  B: He's my *brother* / *sister*.

4 **A:** Who's Holly?
  B: She's my *brother* / *sister*.

5 **A:** Who's Paula?
  B: *He's* / *She's* my sister.

Short and long forms

3 Write the long forms.

1 What's your name?
  What is your name?
  ....

2 My name's Liz.
  ....

3 I'm Billy.
  ....

4 He's my brother.
  ....

5 She's my sister.
  ....

Greetings

4a Write sentences.

1 morning, Stone. Good Mrs

Good morning, Mrs Stone.

2 afternoon, Mr Parsons. I'm Jane. Good

....

3 Smith. name's Jon. evening, My Good Miss

....

4 Good I'm Liz. morning, White. Mr

....

5 Miss to evening, Roberts. Good Welcome Bristol!

....

6 London! to Good Mrs Brown. afternoon, Welcome

....

4b Write the conversations. Use *Good morning, Good afternoon, Goodbye* or *Good evening*.

1 *Good afternoon.* ....

2 ....

3 ....

4 ....

Her name's Jodie.

Family

1 Complete the chart.

Feminine	Masculine
aunt	¹ *uncle* ....
²	brother
mother	³ ....
⁴	son
⁵	husband
⁶	grandfather

2 Look at the family tree. Complete the sentences.

Hi. My name's Sam and this is my family. Jenny is my ¹ *mum* and ² .... is my dad. My sister is ³ .... ⁴ .... is my aunt and David is my ⁵ .... My cousin is ⁶ ....

Sam

Family + *my*

3 Look at the family tree in Exercise 2. Complete the sentences.

I'm Laura. ¹ .... is George. Steve is ² .... son and Helen is ³ ....

Laura

I'm Ben. ⁴ .... is George. ⁵ .... uncle is ⁶ .... Jenny is ⁷ .... Jess is my ⁸ ....

Ben

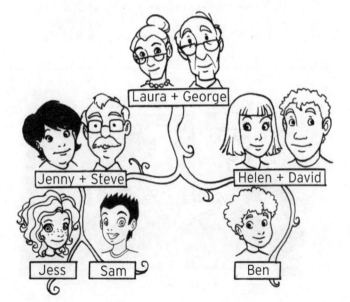

Laura + George

Jenny + Steve

Helen + David

Jess   Sam

Ben

4 **Look at the photos.**
Complete the conversations.

 ①
Jake

②
Lucy

③
Rob

④
Jodie

⑤
Duke

⑥
Leo

1 **A:** What's _his_ name?
   B: _His name's_ Jake.

2 **A:** What's .... name?
   B: _Her_ ....

3 **A:** .... ?
   B: ....

4 **A:** .... ?
   B: ....

5 **A:** .... ?
   B: ....

6 **A:** .... ?
   B: ....

he/she and *his/her*

5a **Complete the conversations.**

> Her   He   she   ~~Her~~   She   His   he

A: Is this your sister?
B: Yes. [1] _Her_ name's Cath.
   [2] ....'s very clever.

A: Who is this?
B: [3] ....'s my brother.
   [4] .... name's Paul.

A: Is this your mother?
B: No, [5] ....'s my aunt.
   [6] .... name's Trisha.
   And [7] ....'s my uncle.
   His name's Roger.

5b **Circle the correct word.**

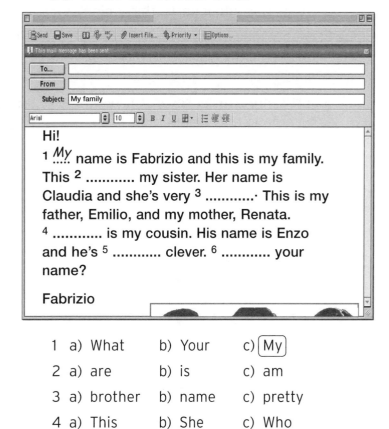

1 a) What   b) Your   c) My
2 a) are   b) is   c) am
3 a) brother   b) name   c) pretty
4 a) This   b) She   c) Who
5 a) very   b) is   c) friendly
6 a) Who's   b) What's   c) Is

3 How old are you?

Numbers 1–50

1a Write the missing numbers.

1 three × six = *eighteen*

2 nineteen − *eight* = eleven

3 one + twelve = ...

4 twenty − .... = five

5 sixteen + four = ...

6 three + nine + ... = fourteen

7 .... − thirteen = six

8 ten ÷ two = ...

1b Draw lines between the numbers. What's the secret word?

Line 1: twenty-eight, twenty-seven, thirty-three, thirty-four, forty, thirty-nine.

Line 2: twenty-nine, thirty-five, forty-one, forty-two, thirty-six, thirty, twenty-nine.

Line 3: forty-three, thirty-seven, thirty-one, forty-four, thirty-eight, thirty-two.

```
•21   •22   •23   •24   •25   •26

•27   •28   •29   •30   •31   •32

•33   •34   •35   •36   •37   •38

•39   •40   •41   •42   •43   •44

•45   •46   •47   •48   •49   •50
```

The secret word is: ....

Verb *to be*

2 Complete the conversation.

Teacher: 1 *Are you* Sam Tyler?

Sam: Yes, 2 .... 3 .... Mr Reed?

Teacher: No, 4 .... 5 .... Mr Parker! 6 .... in Year 7, Sam?

Sam: Yes, 7 ....

Teacher: Then you're in my class!

3 Write the questions.

1 **A:** *Are you Hannah Dodds?*
    (you/Hannah Dodds)
    B: Yes, I am.

2 **A:** ....
    (how old/you)
    B: I'm twelve.

3 **A:** ....
    (you/in Year 8)
    B: Yes, I am.

4 **A:** ....
    (you/at Northgate School)
    B: No, I'm not. I'm at Parkdale School.

Asking how old people are

4 Look at the pictures. Write questions and answers.

① 7
② 13
③ 19
④ 25
⑤ 33
⑥ 42
⑦ 50

1 **A:** *How old is he?* ....
  B: *He's seven.* ....

2 **A:** *How old is she?* ....
  B: ....

3 **A:** ....
  B: ....

4 **A:** ....
  B: ....

5 **A:** ....
  B: ....

6 **A:** ....
  B: ....

7 **A:** ....
  B: ....

5 Complete the questions and answers.

'm   am   's   'm not   is   ~~are~~   Are

1 **A:** How old *are.* you?
  B: I .... twelve.

2 **A:** How old .... he?
  B: He .... ten.

3 **A:** .... you eleven years old?
  B: Yes, I ....·

4 **A:** Are you nine?
  B: No, I ....· I'm eleven.

Song

Uncle Trevor and Auntie Kitty

6 🎧02 Listen. Complete the song.

Here's a photo of my uncle,
And [1] .... name is Trevor Lee.
He is friendly and he is clever,
('Good morning, Tom') and
    he is forty-three.

Trevor, you're very clever,
You're so friendly too.
Clever Trevor [2] .... my uncle,
But my best friend is you.

Here's a photo of my auntie,
And her name is Kitty Dunn.
[3] .... is friendly and she is pretty,
('Hello, dear') and she is
    forty-one.

Kitty, you're very pretty,
You're so friendly too.
Pretty Kitty is [4] .... auntie,
But my best friend is you.

Go to page 94 to see the completed song.

4 Skills practice

Reading

1 Read the text. Write the names, ages and nationalities of the people in the pictures.

....

....

....

....

....

....

Hi! My name's Kelly. I'm British. I'm thirteen and I'm from Newcastle. She's my sister. Her name's Lauren. She's sixteen years old and she's very nice. He's my brother. His name's Darren. He's nine years old. He's naughty! He's my father. His name's Ken. He's fifty. And she's my mum. Her name's Anne. She isn't British, she's American. She's forty-two. This is my teacher. His name's Mr Allen. He's from Australia. He's twenty-eight years old. And this is my friend. His name's Chris. He's thirteen years old. He's Canadian.

Kelly, 13, British
....

....

....

....

....

....

....

2 Match the people in Exercise 1 with their countries.

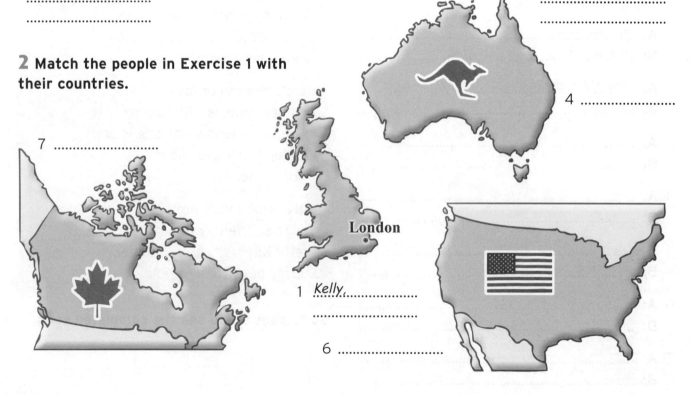

4 ....

7 ....

London

1 *Kelly,*...............

....

6 ....

STUDY TIP!

It's a good idea to learn words in groups.

3 Put the words in the correct groups.

~~father~~   ~~teacher~~   ~~daughter~~   brother
friend   uncle   mother   cousin
aunt   son   parent

①   ② ③

father	daughter	teacher
......	......	......
......	......	......
......	......	......

Listening

4 🎧 **(03)** Listen to Ann. Match the person with their name and age.

Relationship	Name	Age
1 sister	a) Boston	30
2 father	b) Fred	14
3 mother	c) Mr Foster	3
4 cat	d) Richard	45
5 friend	e) Sally	13
6 teacher	f) Pat	42

1   _e 14_   2   3   ....
4   5   6   ....

Writing

Portfolio

5 In your notebook, draw a picture and write about your family and friends.

This is a picture of ...
He's ...   years old.
He's my ...
He's very ...

....

Cartoon Time: Future World

6 Complete the conversation.
Use the words in the box.

Are   to   Bye   too   you   Hi   Yes
my   here   name's

Zar: ¹ _Hi,_ I'm Zar.
Mixi: Hello. My ² .... Mixi.
Zar: Welcome ³ .... Bristol!
Mixi: Thank ⁴ ....·

Zar: ⁵ .... you in Year 7?
Mixi: ⁶ ....· I am.
Zar: Me ⁷ ....· Look, here's Maz. She's
⁸ .... sister.
Mixi: OK. Rover, come ⁹ ....· Good dog.

Mixi: ROVER! COME HERE! Goodbye, Zar.
Zar: ¹⁰ ....·

5 Revision

1 Find the stickers.

1 Good morning, Mrs Hatch.

2 Good evening, Mr Brown.

3 Good afternoon, Miss Kent.

4 Good morning, Mr Helman.

5 Good afternoon, Mr Whitman.

6 Good evening, Mrs Smith.

Score ___ /5

2 Put the letters in the correct order.

1 danfrgrehta = *grandfather*

2 ecnul = ...

3 uertghda = ...

4 tanu = ...

5 rrobteh = ...

6 rergohnmadt = ...

7 retahf = ...

8 ounisc = ...

Score ___ /7

3 Write introductions.

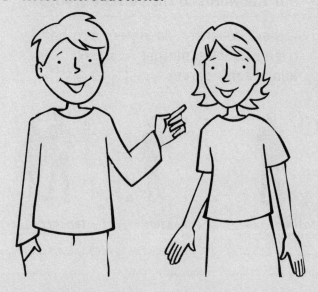

1 Leo Rocca/Jodie Rocca
Leo: *This is my sister. Her name's Jodie.*

2 Jodie Rocca/Leo Rocca
Jodie: ....

3 Lucy Barr/Ian Barr
Lucy: ....

4 Sharon Rocca/Jodie Rocca
Sharon: ....

5 Sharon Rocca/Leo Rocca
Sharon: ....

6 Lucy Barr/Miss Ben
Lucy: ....

Score ___ /5

4 Answer the questions.

a) 17 + 8 = *twenty-five*

b) 9 + 4 = ...

c) 29 − 10 = ...

d) 13 − 7 + 15 = ...

e) 40 − 11 + 9 = ...

f) 21 + 23 = ...

g) 12 + 25 − 3 + 16 = ...

Score ___ /6

5 Write the first word in each question.

1 *How.* old are you?

2 ....'s he?

3 .... your sister in Year 8?

4 ....'s your name?

5 .... you in my class?

6 .... old is your sister?

7 .... he your brother?

Score ___ /6

6 Circle the correct words.

A: This is my family. This is Kirsty.
  [1] *She /* She's */ Is* my sister.

B: How old [2] *a / are / is* she?

A: She's ten. And this is my mother.
  [3] *My / Her / His* name's Brenda.

B: How old is [4] *your / you're / you* brother?

A: [5] *She / He / He's* fourteen.

B: And this is you. How old [6] *are /am / is* you?

A: I'm twelve.

Score ___ /5

7 Match a sentence in A to a sentence in B.

Ⓐ

1 Hello, Uma.

2 See you later.

3 Welcome to Bristol!

4 I'm twelve.

5 Are you hungry?

6 Who is she?

7 Is Rover your dog?

Ⓑ

a) Thank you.

b) She's my teacher.

c) Hi, Dave.

d) Yes. He's very friendly.

e) Yes, I am.

f) OK. Bye.

g) Me too.

1	c	2		3		4	

5		6		7	

Score ___ /6

Check your score

TOTAL ___ /40

Brilliant! (30–40)

Good! (20–29)

OK (10–19)

6 They're American.

Countries and nationalities

1 Complete the crossword. Find the secret country.

1 Luka's Greek. He's from ....

2 They're Argentinian. They're from ....

3 He's Turkish. He's from ....

4 Ana's Spanish. She's from ....

5 He's French. He's from ....

6 We're Italian. We're from ....

		¹G	R	E	E	C	E
2							
	³T						
		M					
4							
5							
6							

The secret country is ....

2 Complete the chart with the country or nationality.

Country	Nationality
1 Russia	*Russian*
2 *China*	Chinese
3 Portugal	....
4 the UK	....
5	Polish
6 the USA	....
7	Brazilian
8 France	....
9 Spain	....
10	Canadian

Asking where people are from

3 Complete the sentences with *am*, *is* or *are*. Use short forms.

1 We ´re Italian.

2 Matthew .... American.

3 Where .... you from?

4 .... they from Brazil?

5 .... Teresa from Milan?

6 Jenny and her sister .... from the UK.

7 I .... Spanish.

8 .... you and your family from Turkey?

4 Complete the conversation.

Teacher 1: ¹ *Is* Donna from the USA?

Teacher 2: Yes, she ² ....·

Teacher 1: ³ .... Mark and Dan American too?

Teacher 2: No, they ⁴ ....· They're from the UK.

Teacher 1: ⁵ .... Ross British?

Teacher 2: No, he ⁶ ....·

Teacher 1: ⁷ .... Laura and Mauro Italian?

Teacher 2: Yes, they ⁸ ....·

Questions and nationalities

5 Look at the pictures. Complete the conversations.

① ¡Hola! — Spain

② Hi! — the USA

③ Cześć! — Poland

④ Hello! — the UK

⑤ Buongiorno! — Italy

⑥ Bonjour! — France

1 **Teacher:** *Where are you from?*
  Miguel: *I'm from Spain.*

2 **Teacher:** *Where are you from?*
  Jodie and Jessie: *We're from the USA.*

3 **Teacher:** ....
  Aldona: ....

4 **Teacher:** ....
  Chris and Tom: ....

5 **Teacher:** ....
  Claudia and Barbara: ....

6 **Teacher:** ....
  Pierre: ....

6 Look at Exercise 5 again. Write the questions and answers.

1 **A:** *Where is Miguel from?*
  B: *He's from Spain.*

2 **A:** *Where are Jodie and Jessie from?*
  B: *They're from the USA.*

3 **A:** ....
  B: ....

4 **A:** ....
  B: ....

5 **A:** ....
  B: ....

6 **A:** ....
  B: ....

7 Write the questions and answers.

1 **A:** *Is she American?*
  (Madonna/the USA?)
  B: *Yes, she is.* (✓)

2 **A:** *Are they Canadian?*
  (Prince William and Prince Harry/Canada?)
  B: .... (✗)

3 **A:** ....
  (Ronaldo/Brazil?)
  B: .... (✓)

4 **A:** ....
  (Brad Pitt and Angelina Jolie/France?)
  B: .... (✗)

5 **A:** ....
  (Kylie Minogue/Spain?)
  B: .... (✗)

6 **A:** ....
  (Harry Potter and Ron Weasley/the UK?)
  B: .... (✓)

7 Is it an orange tree?

Everyday objects

1 Complete the words.

1 d *esk*	7 c ....
2 a	8 h ....
3 o .... t	9 t ....
4 o	10 i c
5 e	11 m ....
6 b	12 c ....

a/an

2 Find the objects in Exercise 1. Write sentences with *a* or *an*.

1 *It's a desk.*	7 ....
2 *It's an apple.*	8 ....
3	9 ....
4	10 ....
5	11 ....
6	12 ....

this/that

3 Write questions and answers.

1 *What's that?*
  It's a house.

2 ....?
  ....

3 ....?
  ....

4 ....?
  ....

5 ....?
  ....

6 ....?
  ....

we/they and *our/their*

4 Circle the correct words.

1 ⌐They're⌐ / *Their* Pat and Ken.
2 It's *we're* / *our* car.
3 That's *they're* / *their* house.
4 *We're* / *Our* from the USA.
5 Is that *they're* / *their* photo?
6 *They're* / *Their* my sisters.
7 That's *they're* / *their* school.
8 *Our* / *They're* parents aren't at home.

5 Complete the conversation.

> Their   They're   ~~We're~~
> our   we're   their

1 I'm Jenny and she's Sue.
  We're sisters.

2 This is Paul and this is Dean.
  This is .... father, Frank.

3 **A:** Are you and Maria from Italy?
  B: No, ... from Spain.

4 Simon and Paul are brothers.
  .... house is in London.

5 **A:** Who are they?
  B: .... Elliot and Amy.

6 I'm Trevor and this is Jackie.
  This is .... mother, Trudy.

Listening

6 🎧 04 Listen. Number the sentences in the correct order.

☐ **Jodie:** No, it isn't. It's a DVD with photos of our cousins from the USA.

☐ **Leo:** No, we're from New York.

☐ **Jodie:** Yes, it is.

☐ **Leo:** Yes, that's right.

[1] **Leo:** Hi, Rob! Hi, Lucy! Come in.

☐ **Lucy:** Is that their car?

☐ **Leo:** They're from California.

☐ **Lucy:** Cool!

☐ **Jodie:** Look, that's their house.

☐ **Lucy:** Wow! It's really big.

[2] **Lucy:** What's this? Is it a film?

☐ **Rob:** What's that? Is it an orange tree?

☐ **Lucy:** Are you from California too?

People and objects

7 Complete the conversation.

> Are they your cousins?
> Is that their dog?
> ~~Thanks. Is this your computer?~~
> Our computer's really old!
> Who's that?

Elliot: Hi, Amy. Come in.

Amy: [1] *Thanks. Is this your computer?*

Elliot: Yes, it is.

Amy: It's cool. [2] ....

Elliot: Look. This is my family.

Amy: [3] ....

Elliot: That's my aunt. She's from Italy.

Amy: And who are they? [4] ....

Elliot: Yes, they are. Their names are Paola and Federica.

Amy: [5] ....

Elliot: Yes, it is.

8 They're mangoes.

Fruit

1 Find 10 fruits in the puzzle.

P	E	A	C	H	P	E	L	W	M	P
G	D	O	P	E	I	M	E	L	O	N
I	A	L	I	C	F	T	M	I	J	Y
A	M	A	N	G	O	C	O	B	A	D
N	O	L	E	I	T	H	N	U	L	U
S	T	R	A	W	B	E	R	R	Y	T
W	C	I	P	O	K	R	V	E	A	G
E	P	M	P	E	A	R	A	S	I	Y
H	L	O	L	D	S	Y	P	D	F	I
O	U	R	E	O	E	S	O	I	E	K
T	M	I	N	B	G	R	A	P	E	L

Plurals

3 Write the plural of the words in Exercise 2.

1 *mangoes* ....
2 *grapes* ....
3 *cherries* ....
4 ....
5 ....
6 ....
7 ....
8 ....
9 ....

Colours

4 Find eight colours in the wordsnake.

2 Label the pictures.

1 *a mango* ....   2 ....   3 ....

4 ....   5 ....   6 ....

7 ....   8 ....   9 ....

5 Find the stickers.

```
┌    ┐        ┌    ┐        ┌    ┐

└    ┘        └    ┘        └    ┘
```

1 an orange and pink bag   2 a purple and grey bag   3 a yellow and brown bag

```
┌    ┐        ┌    ┐        ┌    ┐

└    ┘        └    ┘        └    ┘
```

4 a red and brown bag   5 a green and yellow bag   6 a pink and purple bag

these/those + plurals

6 Write questions and answers.

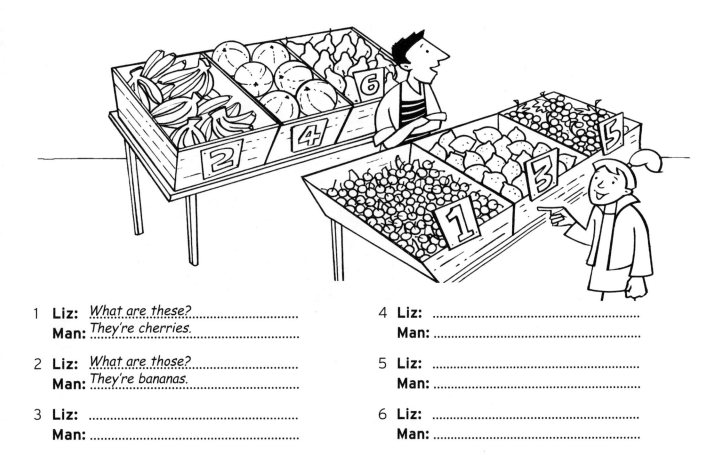

1 **Liz:** *What are these?*
  Man: *They're cherries.*

2 **Liz:** *What are those?*
  Man: *They're bananas.*

3 **Liz:** ....
  Man: ....

4 **Liz:** ....
  Man: ....

5 **Liz:** ....
  Man: ....

6 **Liz:** ....
  Man: ....

 **Skills practice**

1 Read about Lisa and Jerry. Complete the chart.

TO: Jerry Blake
FROM: Lisa Hannigan
SUBJECT: New epal

Hi!
I'm Lisa. I'm twelve. I'm from Cork in the Republic of Ireland. My mum is English and my dad is Irish. Cork is a beautiful city, but it isn't the capital of Ireland. That's Dublin. This is a photo of Cork and a photo of me and my cat! She's very friendly.

Bye for now,
Lisa

Hi Lisa!
Thanks for your email.
I'm Jerry - your new penpal!
I'm thirteen, and I'm Australian.
My sister, Donna, is fifteen.
We aren't from the capital,
Canberra. We're from Sydney.
It's a big, beautiful place.
Here's a picture of the city.

Love from
Jerry

Name	Age	Home country	Nationality	Home city	Capital city
Lisa	12				
Jerry					

2 True (✓) or false (✗)?

Lisa

1 She's fourteen. ✗

2 Her mum is Irish. ☐

3 Cork is a nice place. ☐

4 Her cat is friendly. ☐

Jerry

5 He's from Australia. ☐

6 He's from Canberra. ☐

7 His sister is fifteen. ☐

8 Sydney is big. ☐

Writing

Portfolio

3 Write the text again in your notebook. Use correct capital letters.

> hello. i'm thomas clark. i'm from liverpool in the uk. i'm twelve years old. my friend james is twelve, too. he's american. he's from washington. that's the capital of the usa.

Hello. I'm Thomas Clark. ....

4 Complete the chart.

> ~~Eva~~   Bristol   13
> ~~Jenkins~~ England Laura (16)

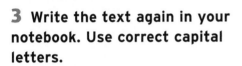

First name:	*Eva*
Surname:	*Jenkins*
Age:	....
Home town:	....
Country:	....
Sister:	....

5 Now write about Eva Jenkins in your notebook.

This is a photo of Eva Jenkins. She's ...

Cartoon Time: Future World

6 Complete the conversation. Use the words in the box.

> that Now it taste ~~Come~~ Yuk right

Ⓐ

Mixi: Hi, Zar!

Zar: Hi, Mixi! ¹ *Come* in.

Mixi: Wow! What's ² ....? Is ³ .... ice cream?

Ⓑ

Zar: That's ⁴ .... Have a ⁵ ....!

Mixi: Thanks. ⁶ ...., is it strawberry or cherry ice cream?

Ⓒ

Mixi: ⁷ ....!

Zar: It's lime and egg ice cream. My favourite!

19

10 Revision

1 Complete the words to make nationalities. Use a, e, i, o or u.

1 Sp_a_n_i_sh
2 It _ l _ _ n
3 P _ l _ s h
4 Br _ t _ s h
5 P _ r t _ g _ _ s _
6 _ m _ r _ c _ n
7 R _ s s _ _ n

Score ___ /6

2 Rearrange the words to make questions and sentences.

1 Where from? you are
Where are you from?

2 is Where from? he
....

3 from Bristol. They are
....

4 they are Where from?
....

5 UK from the They are too.
....
....

6 from Tina and Italy. Frank are
....
....

Score ___ /5

3 Write questions and answers.

1 A: *Is he from Poland?* (he/Poland?)
  B: *Yes, he is.* (✓)

2 A: *Are they from Russia?* (they/Russia?)
  B: *No they aren't. They're from the UK.*
  (✗/the UK)

3 A: .... (she/France?)
  B: ....
  (✗/Germany)

4 A: .... (you/Portugal?)
  B: .... (✓)

5 A: .... (they/Turkey?)
  B: ....
  (✗/Argentina)

6 A: .... (she/Greece?)
  B: .... (✓)

Score ___ /8

4 Complete the sentences with we're, they're, our or their.

1 I'm Mark and this is Tim. And this is _our_ dog, Buster.

2 Rachel and Lisa are new students. .. .. from Bristol.

3 A: Is this Mark and Tim's car?
  B: No, ... car is blue.

4 A: Frank, Hannah, Gina, where are you from?
  B: Frank's from Canada and .... from South Africa.

5 Aunt Jane is in the USA. This is a photo of her son, Paul. He's .... cousin.

Score ___ /4

5 Write sentences.

1 *This is a banana.*

2 *Those are plums.*

3 ....

4 ....

5 ....

6 ....

Score ___ /8

6 Write the colours.

1 black + white = *grey*

2 red + white = ...

3 yellow + red = ...

4 blue + red = ...

5 yellow + blue = ...

Score ___ /4

7 Choose a caption for each picture.

Come in.   ~~Catch!~~   I don't know.   Cool!
Have a taste.   Yuk!

1 *Catch!* ....   4 ....
2 ....   5 ....
3 ....   6 ....

Score ___ /5

TOTAL ___ /40

Check your score

Brilliant! (30–40)
Good! (20–29)
OK (10–19)

Go to page 82 to see Puzzle Story 1.

11 Where is it?

The house

1 Find seven rooms and places in the puzzle.

R	T	A	G	A	R	D	E	N	W	B
I	S	T	A	I	R	S	Q	U	B	E
L	E	O	R	T	U	B	N	G	A	D
Z	J	I	A	T	C	E	E	L	T	R
P	O	L	G	R	V	U	S	T	H	O
E	Y	E	E	R	G	A	U	R	R	O
S	I	T	T	I	N	G	R	O	O	M
Y	G	C	H	A	O	R	T	U	O	M
N	U	M	M	I	D	R	U	S	M	I

2 Find the stickers.

1 She's in the dining room.

2 She's in the kitchen.

3 She's in the bathroom.

4 She's in the garden.

5 She's in the hall.

6 She's in the sitting room.

in/on/under/behind

3 Match the pictures and sentences.

a

b

c

d

1	He's in the car.	c
2	He's under the car.	
3	He's on the car.	
4	He's behind the car.	

4 Look at the picture and complete the sentences.

1 The boy is *behind the chair.* ....
2 The cat is ....
3 The book is ....
4 The bag is ....
5 The fruit is ....
6 The pineapple is ....
7 The mobile phone is ....

the and a/an

6 **Complete the conversation with a or the.**

A: Is that ¹ *a.* photo of your dog?

B: Yes, it is. In this photo, he's in ² ....
garden with ³ .... friend.

A: And what's this photo?

B: It's ⁴ .... photo of my cat, Minky.
She's in ⁵ .... dining room on ⁶ .... chair.

A: And where is she in this photo?

B: She's in ⁷ .... hall. She's on ⁸ ....
stairs.

5 **Look at the picture again. Write questions and answers.**

1 (book/under/table?)
  A: *Where's the book? Is it under the table?*
  B: *No, it isn't.*

2 (cat/behind/bag?)
  A: ....
  B: ....

3 (mobile phone/in/bag?)
  A: ....
  B: ....

4 (bananas/on/table?)
  A: ....
  B: ....

5 (boy/behind/table?)
  A: ....
  B: ....

6 (fruit/on/chair?)
  A: ....
  B: ....

7 (bag/on/table?)
  A: ....
  B: ....

Here's Leo's towel.

Common possessions

1 **Cross out the extra letter in each word. The extra letters spell a secret word.**

			Extra letters
1	camesra	*camera*	*s*
2	phokne	....	......
3	steareo	....	......
4	wattch	....	......
5	CeD	....	......
6	towbel	....	......
7	compuoter	....	......
8	baike	....	......
9	barll	....	......
10	raddio	....	......

The secret word is ....

2 **Complete the puzzle.**

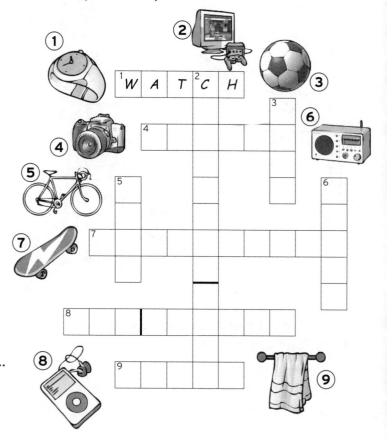

W A T C H

Possessive 's

3 **Say if the things are Hannah's or Elliot's.**

1 *It's Hannah's bike.* .... (bike)
2 .... (skateboard)
3 .... (towel)
4 .... (watch)
5 .... (dog)
6 .... (ball)
7 .... (MP3 player)
8 .... (camera)

4 Look at the pictures. Write sentences.

1 *They're Kate's CDs.*   2 ....

3 ....   4 ....

5 ....   6 ....

5 Rewrite the sentences with apostrophes.

1 Its Tims book.
   It's Tim's book.

2 They arent in the girls football team.
   ....

3 Wheres Billys new mobile phone?
   ....

4 Theyre my parents CDs.
   ....

5 Its Paulas cool bike.
   ....

6 Are they your parents friends?
   ....

7 It isnt Mr Parkers desk.
   ....

6 Complete the conversation.

> ~~are these~~   Dad's   friends'   this
> these aren't   They're

Mum: Sam, ¹ *are these* your things?

Sam: ² .... Jess's CDs, but they're my computer games.

Mum: And what about these DVDs?

Jess: They're ³ .... DVDs.

Mum: But ⁴ .... Dad's books.

Jess: No, they aren't. They're our ⁵ .... books.

Mum: And what about ⁶ .... phone?

Sam: It's your phone, Mum!

Listening

7 (05) **Listen. Complete the conversation.**

Lucy: Here's a ¹ *good* place.

Leo: What about a swim?

Rob: OK. ² .... are the towels?

Lucy: In the bag. Here's Leo's towel.

Leo: Thanks.

Lucy: Oh, good! Here's Rob's MP3 ³ ....

Leo: Where are the boys' changing ⁴ ....?

Rob: They're ⁵ .... the café. Come on!

Kim: I'm bored. Where's my ⁶ ....?

Lucy: Sorry, Kim. It's at ⁷ ....·

Kim: Oh, no!

Lucy: ⁸ .... mind! ⁹ .... have a swim.

25

13 There are fifteen bathrooms!

House and furniture

1a Complete the puzzle. Find the secret word.

	¹P	L	A	N	T	
²W		N		O		
	³		H	A	R	
⁴P		S		E	R	
	⁵C		P			A	R	D
⁶W	A		D		O		E
	⁷B		D			

The secret word is: ....

1b Look at the picture in Exercise 2. Label the things in the house.

1 _sofa_ ....
2 _cupboard_ ....
3 ....
4 ....
5 ....
6 ....
7 ....
8 ....

there is a/there are some

2 Look at the picture again. Write sentences with *there is a* or *there are some*.

1 _There is a sofa._ ....
2 _There are some cupboards._ ....
3 ....
4 ....

5 ....
6 ....
7 ....
8 ....

there's a/there isn't a/there are some/there aren't any

3 Look at the picture of Amy's bedroom. Write sentences with *there*.

1 (bed)   *There's a bed.*

2 (books) ....

3 (window) ....

4 (computer) ....

5 (television) ....

6 (posters) ....

7 (plants) ....

8 (wardrobe) ....

4 Look at the picture in Exercise 3 again. Write questions and answers with *there*.

1 **A:** *Is there a bed?* .... (bed)
  B: *Yes, there is.* ....

2 **A:** .... (posters)
  B: ....

3 **A:** .... (plants)
  B: ....

4 **A:** .... (sofa)
  B: ....

5 **A:** .... (cupboards)
  B: ....

6 **A:** .... (wardrobe)
  B: ....

7 **A:** .... (books)
  B: ....

8 **A:** .... (stereo)
  B: ....

Song

The Eight-Year-Old Rock Star

5 〔06〕 Listen. Complete the song.

I'm in my room, on my bed, [1]............... a poster
  on my wall.
It's a poster of a great pop star and his name
  is Jon Paul.
Jon Paul's band is very cool, [2]............... songs
  are really great.
Jon Paul's band is the best in town, but Jon
  Paul's only eight!

Oh Jon Paul, oh eight-year-old Jon Paul,
Your [3]............... name is *Rocking Gold*,
And you are very cool!

I'm in my room, the TV's on, [4]............... a pop
  star on TV.
The pop star's from a famous band but his
  band's not for me.
The pop [5]............... name is still Jon Paul, his
  band's still *Rocking Gold*,
But Jon Paul's band just isn't cool 'cos now
  he's nine years old.

Oh Jon Paul, oh nine-year-old Jon Paul,
You're not so great now you're not eight,
And your band's not so [6]................

Go to page 94 to see the completed song.

27

skills practice

Reading

1 Read about three houses. Write the name of the house under the picture.

....

....

....

FOREST LODGE

Forest Lodge is in the mountains in Scotland. There's a kitchen, a bathroom, a sitting room and three bedrooms. There isn't a dining room, but there are big windows and beautiful views. There's a little garage and a garden. It's very warm and comfortable in winter.

ABERDOWER CASTLE

Aberdower Castle is a very big holiday home in Wales. There are twenty-five rooms! There are eight bedrooms, three sitting rooms and six bathrooms. And there are two kitchens! The table in the dining room is very big, with twenty chairs. There's a very big garden but there aren't any garages.

PARADISE VILLA

Paradise Villa is in Cornwall. It's very big. There are five bedrooms, three bathrooms, a big kitchen, a dining room and a sitting room. It's light and cool. Outside there is a garden and a swimming pool. There are two garages.

> **New words**
> mountains
> view
> warm
> comfortable
> castle
> light
> cool
> outside

2 Complete the chart.

	bedrooms	bathroom(s)	kitchen(s)	sitting room(s)	dining room	garden	garage(s)	swimming pool
Forest Lodge	3				yes / no	yes / no	yes / no	yes / no
Aberdower Castle	8				yes / no	yes / no	yes / no	yes / no
Paradise Villa	5				yes / no	yes / no	yes / no	yes / no

STUDY TIP!

Sometimes you can learn new words with their opposites.

3 Find pairs of opposites in the text on page 28.

big ....,' ....

.......................,' ....

.......................,' ....

Listening

4 (07) Listen to Mr Darling. He is the butler at Cranley House. Are the sentences true (T) or false (F)? Write true sentences.

1 There are 38 rooms in Cranley House. **F**
There are 48 rooms in Cranley House.
....

2 There are 6 sitting rooms. ☐
....

3 There are 6 dining rooms. ☐
....

4 There's a big garden. ☐
....

5 There are 22 bedrooms. ☐
....

6 His bedroom is big. ☐
....

7 There is a wardrobe in his bedroom. ☐
....

8 There's a television in his bedroom. ☐
....

Writing

Portfolio

5 You are Mr Darling. Write about Cranley House.

There are forty-eight rooms in Cranley House.
There are ...
....

Cartoon Time: Future World

6 Complete the conversation.
Use the words in the box.

fun ~~What~~ Never very Oh about on

Mixi: I'm bored.
Robomo: ¹ *What* about a game of football? Come ² ....! It's great!
Mixi: No, football isn't cool.

Mixi: I'm ³ .... bored.
Robomo: OK. What ⁴ .... a game of cricket? It's ⁵ ....!
Mixi: No. It's a boy's game.

Robomo: OK. ⁶ .... mind. What about ...
Mixi: What about watching TV?
Robomo: ⁷ .... no!

15 Revision

1 Complete the sentences with *a/an* or *the* and a word in the box.

armchair   bathroom   dog   ~~garage~~
woman   television

1 The car is in .....the garage........
2 There's ....
   in the kitchen.
3 A cat is on ....
   in the sitting room.
4 There's ....
   on the bed in a bedroom.
5 A dog is in ....
6 A cat and ....
   are in the bedroom.

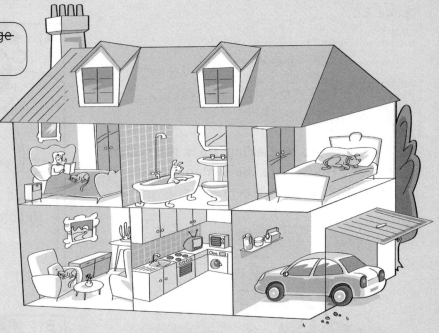

Score ____ /10

2 Look at the picture. Write five sentences.

1 *The bag is on the chair.*
   ....
   (bag/chair)
2 ....
   ....
   (mobile phone/bag)
3 ....
   ....
   (books/chair)
4 ....
   ....
   (apple/chair)
5 ....
   ....
   (girl/chair)

Score ____ /4

3 Find eight words.

D	E	C	O	M	P	U	T	E	R
A	F	S	W	C	B	I	K	E	R
T	P	C	A	M	E	R	A	N	A
S	K	A	T	E	B	O	A	R	D
D	E	S	C	M	B	A	L	L	I
Q	R	B	H	S	T	E	R	E	O

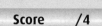

1 *ball*   4 ....   7 ....
2 .... 5 ....   8 ....
3 .... 6 ....

Score ____ /7

30

4 Look at the pictures. Make sentences.

1 Mr Potter
It's Mr Potter's armchair.

2 the boys
They're the boys' posters.

3 the girls
....
....

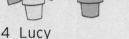
4 Lucy
....
....

5 Mrs Reed
....
....

6 Jamie
....
....

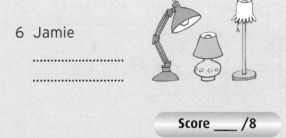

Score ___ /8

5 Complete the email with the words and phrases in the box.

aren't   Are there any   there's   ~~There are~~
there are some   Is there   there isn't

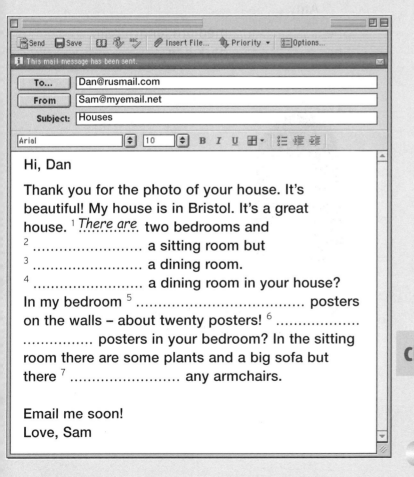

Send Save   Insert File... Priority ▾ Options...

ℹ This mail message has been sent.   ✉

To... | Dan@rusmail.com
From | Sam@myemail.net
Subject: | Houses

Arial ▾ | 10 ▾ | B I U ▦▾ | ☰ ☰ ☰

Hi, Dan

Thank you for the photo of your house. It's beautiful! My house is in Bristol. It's a great house. ¹ *There are* two bedrooms and
² .... a sitting room but
³ .... a dining room.
⁴ .... a dining room in your house?
In my bedroom ⁵ .... posters on the walls – about twenty posters! ⁶ ....
.... posters in your bedroom? In the sitting room there are some plants and a big sofa but there ⁷ .... any armchairs.

Email me soon!
Love, Sam

Score ___ /6

6 Make phrases from the words in column A and column B.

Ⓐ   Ⓑ
1 I'm ———————— know.
2 What about ——— bored.
3 I don't   mind.
4 Oh   a game of football?
5 Never   on.
6 Come   no!

1 *I'm bored.* ....
2 ....
....
3 ....
4 ....
5 ....
6 ....

Score ___ /5

TOTAL ___ /40

Check your score

Brilliant! (30–40)
Good! (20–29)
OK (10–19)

31

16 I've got green eyes.

Hair styles and colours

1 Complete the chart.

| ~~straight~~ ~~long~~ ~~black~~ blond brown |
| curly dark fair grey wavy |
| medium length red short spiky |

1	2	3
long	*straight*	*black*
....	....	....
....	....	....
	....	....
		....
		....
		....

have got

2 Write the long form.

1 I've got three sisters.
   I have got three sisters.

2 She hasn't got a bike.
   ....

3 We haven't got a computer.
   ....

4 My mum's got blue eyes.
   ....

5 I haven't got any animals.
   ....

6 He's got long black hair.
   ....

7 They've got spiky hair.
   ....

8 You've got a new computer.
   ....

3 Look at the pictures. Complete the sentences with *has got* or *hasn't got*.

①

Sam

He *hasn't got* fair hair.
He .... spiky hair.

②

Amy

She .... medium length hair.
She .... dark hair.

③

Hannah

She .... blonde hair.
She .... wavy hair.

4 Complete the conversation.

Evan: ¹ *Have you got* dark hair?

Hooey: ² *Yes, I have.*

Evan: ³ *Have you got* spiky hair?

Hooey: ⁴ *No, I haven't.*

Evan: ⁵ .... straight hair?

Hooey: ⁶ ....

Evan: ⁷ .... curly hair?

Hooey: ⁸ ....

Evan: ⁹ .... long hair?

Hooey: ¹⁰ ....

Evan: Are you pretty?

Hooey: Yes, very pretty.

5 Find the stickers.

1 **Jim:** long dark hair and brown eyes

2 **Karen:** curly blonde hair and brown eyes

3 **Julie:** spiky red hair and blue eyes

4 **Paul:** medium length brown hair and green eyes

5 **Poppy:** wavy black hair and brown eyes

6 **Hal:** short blonde hair and blue eyes

7 **Ruth:** straight fair hair and green eyes

8 **Fred:** curly grey hair and brown eyes

6 Look at the stickers in Exercise 5. Write the questions and answers.

1 **You:** *What colour eyes have you got?*
.... (eyes)

Jim: *I've got brown eyes.*

2 **You:** *What colour hair have you got?*
.... (hair)

Karen: *I've got blonde hair.*

3 **You:** ....
.... (hair)

Julie: ....

4 **You:** ....
.... (eyes)

Paul: ....

5 **You:** ....
.... (eyes)

Poppy: ....

6 **You:** ....
.... (eyes)

Hal: ....

7 **You:** ....
.... (hair)

Ruth: ....

8 **You:** ....
.... (hair)

Fred: ....

17 How many chicks ...?

Animals

1 Complete the words.

1 h _o_ _r_ _s_ e	7 l _ _ b
2 g _ _ t	8 d _ _ _ _
3 s _ _ _ p	9 c _ _ _ k
4 ch _ _ _ _ _ n	10 p _ _ _
5 g _ _ _ e	11 c _ _
6 c _ _ f	

Plurals

2 Write the plurals of the animals in Exercise 1.

1 _horses_	7 ....
2	8 ....
3	9 ....
4	10 ....
5	11 ....
6	

Numbers 50–100

3 Write the numbers and animals.

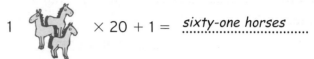

1   × 20 + 1 =   _sixty-one horses_ ....

2   × 20 + 5 = ...

3   × 30 + 9 = ...

4   × 10 + 7 = ...

5   × 20 − 3 = ...

6   × 20 = ...

have got + some/any/ How many?

4 Write the conversations.

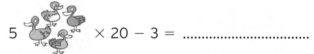

1 **A:** (you and your brother/DVDs?)
Have you and your brother got any DVDs?
....
B: (✓) _Yes, we have._ ....

2 **A:** (Jess and Sam/cousins?)
....
B: (✓) ....

3 **A:** (Mr and Mrs Tyler/computer games?)
....
B: (✗) ....

4 **A:** (you and your friends/animals?)
....
B: (✗) ....

5 **Complete the conversation with the correct forms of *have got*.**

Sophie: How many sheep [1] *have you got?*

Farmer: We [2] .... about forty sheep.

Sophie: And [3] .... any lambs?

Farmer: No, [4] ....

Sophie: [5] .... any ponies?

Farmer: No, [6] ....

Sophie: [7] .... any cows?

Farmer: Yes, [8] ....

Sophie: How many [9] ....?

Farmer: [10] .... about thirty cows, but [11] .... any calves.

Sophie: How many dogs [12] ....?

Farmer: [13] .... two dogs.

6 **Complete the sentences about the farm in Exercise 5. Use *have got*, *some* and *any*.**

They've got about forty sheep and about thirty cows, but .... ponies, lambs or calves. .... dogs.

How many animals ...?

7 **Complete the conversation.**

> **FIONA AND GILL'S PETS**
> cats: 2   dogs: 3   sheep: 1   hamsters: 3

Justin: [1] *Have you and Gill got any pets*, Fiona?

Fiona: [2] .... · We've got nine pets!

Justin: [3] ....?

Fiona: Yes, we have. We've got two.

Justin: And how many dogs have you got?

Fiona: [4] ....·

Justin: Have you got any horses?

Fiona: [5] ....· But we've got a sheep! And some hamsters.

Justin: [6] ....?

Fiona: Three!

Song

Where is Claire?

8 (08) **Listen. Complete the song.**

I'm at the house,
Of my friend Claire,
And Claire [1] ....
Long fair hair.
I knock, knock, knock,
But Claire's [2] .... there.
Oh, where is Claire,
With the long fair hair?

Claire's [3] .... a friend,
He's a big film star,
And the big film star
Has got a [4] ....·
I wait, wait, wait
For Claire and the star,
But they're very far
In the star's [5] .... car.

Go to page 95 to see the completed song.

18 What time is it?

The time

1a Draw the time on the clocks.

1 It's quarter past two.

2 It's three o'clock.

3 It's half past eight.

4 It's quarter to six.

5 It's ten past twelve.

6 It's twenty-five to four.

1b Follow the lines to answer the questions.

1 **You:** What's the time, Liz?
   Liz: *It's half past seven.* ....

2 **You:** What time is it, Billy?
   Billy: ....

3 **You:** What's the time, Paula?
   Paula: ....

4 **You:** What time is it, Peter?
   Peter: ....

5 **You:** What's the time, Robogirl?
   Robogirl: ....

6 **You:** What time is it, Patrick?
   Patrick: ....

Days of the week

2 Complete the days of the week and write them in the correct order.

1 *Monday* ....
2 ....
3 ....
4 ....
5 ....
6 ....
7 ....

Monday S_nday
T_u_sday
T_e_day S_t_rday
W_d_e_day F_iday

36

on + day/at + time

3a Answer the questions.

1 **A:** When's *The Simpsons*?
  B: *It's on Monday at ten to six.*

2 **A:** When's *Mickey and Pluto*?
  B: ....

3 **A:** When's *Cow and Bird*?
  B: ....

4 **A:** When's *Tom and Jerry*?
  B: ....

5 **A:** When's *Jackie Chan*?
  B: ....

6 **A:** When's *The Banana Boys*?
  B: ....

Cartoons on TV next week

	Channel 1	Channel 2
Monday	16:00 Donald Duck	17:50 The Simpsons
Tuesday	15:15 Tom and Jerry	17:20 FutureWorld
Wednesday	16:30 Antz	18:25 Cow and Bird
Thursday	16:45 Ninja Girls	18:40 Jackie Chan
Friday	17:10 Penny's Ponies	17:05 Scooby Doo
Saturday	08:15 Mickey and Pluto	09:10 SpiderMan
Sunday	08:55 Superman	09:45 The Banana Boys

3b Complete with *on* or *at*.

Billy: What's the time?

Peter: It's quarter past five.

Billy: It's *The Simpsons* [1] *at* ten to six.

Peter: No, it's not. *The Simpsons* is [2] .... Monday. It's Tuesday today. It's *FutureWorld* tonight [3] .... twenty past five.

Billy: Cool! *FutureWorld* is great.

Peter: And [4] .... ten past five [5] .... Thursday it's *Penny's Ponies*. It's great too!

Billy: *Penny's Ponies*! Don't be silly! It's not funny and it's not cool. And it's not [6] .... Thursday. It's [7] .... Friday.

Peter: It's only a joke!

Listening

4 🎧 09 Listen. Complete the conversation.

Rob: [1] *We're late.* Hurry up!

Eric: Why? [2] ....?

Rob: It's five to two.

Eric: It's OK, Rob. [3] .... We've got five minutes.

Rob: Two tickets for the match, please.

Man: Sorry, [4] ....

Rob: Oh no! [5] ....?

Man: It's on Sunday at three o'clock.

Eric: He's right. Look at the poster!

Rob: [6] ...., Eric!

Eric: Rob, you're hopeless!

Reading

1 Read about five houses.
Complete the descriptions with the correct word.

cottage   detached   flat
~~semi-detached~~   terraced

1 HARRIET
We've got a
semi-detached
house. It's in Perth in
Scotland, near the river.
Perth is a nice place.
It's a quiet town. We've
got a garage, a garden,
and there are some nice
views from my bedroom.

2 DAN
We've got a .... in
Manchester, in the north of
England. The flat is in a big block.
There are five floors. Our flat is
near the top. It's OK. It's noisy in
the day, but quiet at night.

3 EMMA
My home is a small
.... house in Cardiff,
the capital city of Wales.
Our house has got a small
garden, and it's near a
park. There are three girls
in our family, but we've
only got three bedrooms.
I'm in a bedroom with my
little sister.

4 ROB
Our home is a
.... house in
Woking, in the south
of England. It's got
three bedrooms, two
bathrooms, a sitting
room and a big dining
room. There's a little
garden.

5 TANYA
Our house is a .... in Dorset,
in the west of England. We're lucky! It's
a beautiful home and the countryside is
very quiet. We haven't got a dining room
or a garage, and the bedrooms are very
small, but it's a fantastic house.

2 Complete the sentences with the names of the people in Exercise 1.

1 _Dan_.'s home is in a block of flats.

2 .... has got a beautiful old English house.

3 .... 's home is noisy in the afternoon.

4 .... has got two sisters.

5 ....'s bedroom has got good views.

6 ....'s house has got two bathrooms.

7 ....'s house is in Wales.

8 ....'s house is near a river.

Portfolio

Cartoon Time: Future World

6 Complete the conversation. Use the words in the box.

look   silly   many   About
Sorry   ~~late~~   haven't   joke

WRITING TIPS!

PUNCTUATION

- Put a full stop at the end of a sentence and start the next word with a capital letter.
- Join a list of more than two things with a comma.

3 Write the description in your notebook, using capital letters, full stops and commas.

> my name's Adam i'm twelve years old our home is a detached house it's very big there are five bedrooms three bathrooms and two sitting rooms there's a big garden with a swimming pool trees tables and chairs there are three garages

My name's Adam. I'm ...

4 Pretend you live in one of these houses. Complete the chart.

Type of house:	....
Number of rooms:	....
Number of bedrooms:	....
Other rooms:	....
Garage?	....
Garden?	....
Quiet/noisy?	....

5 In your notebook, write a description of your house in Exercise 4.

Mixi: Hello, Zar.
Zar: Hello, Mixi. You're [1] *late* ....
Mixi: [2] .... , Zar.

Mixi: Have you got any cats or dogs?
Zar: No, I [3] .... But I've got some sheep. Come and [4] ....!
Mixi: Sheep! How [5] .... have you got?

Zar: [6] .... ten.
Mixi: Don't be [7] ....!
Zar: It's only a [8] ....!

20 Revision

1 Tick the two words that match the pictures.

1
- [ ] short
- [✓] wavy
- [ ] straight
- [✓] dark

2
- [ ] spiky
- [ ] short
- [ ] fair
- [ ] medium length

3
- [ ] wavy
- [ ] black
- [ ] straight
- [ ] medium length

4
- [ ] curly
- [ ] long
- [ ] brown
- [ ] blonde

5
- [ ] curly
- [ ] long
- [ ] brown
- [ ] blonde

Score ___ /8

2 Complete the Internet conversation with 've, 's, have, has, haven't or hasn't.

Topic: Hairstyles

10 Users
Sally Jane
Trisha55
Maisy
Robert
Jack
CJ
Tim
Jo
Emma
Zack

\<Sally Jane\> What colour hair [1] _have_ you got?

\<Trisha55\> I [2] .... got brown hair.

\<Sally Jane\> [3] .... your sister got brown hair too?

\<Trisha55\> No, she [4] ....· She [5] .... got red hair and it's very curly. My hair is straight. [6] .... you got straight hair?

\<Sally Jane\> No, I [7] ....· I [8] .... got wavy green hair.

\<Trisha55\> Green hair??

\<Sally Jane\> Yes. Green is my favourite colour!

Score ___ /7

40

3 Write the numbers and plurals.

1 65 / calf
sixty-five calves

2 78 / cow
....

3 51 / sheep
....

4 90 / pony
....

5 100 / goose
....

Score ____ /8

4 Put the words in the correct order.

1 any They ducks. got haven't
They haven't got any ducks.

2 got horses. some We've
....

3 they any Have sheep? got
....

4 about hundred got We've a goats.
....
....

5 got? many ponies How have they
....
....

6 cows. any got They haven't
....

7 hasn't chicks. She any got
....

Score ____ /6

5 Complete the conversation.

on it It's At to 's

Tony: What time is ¹ *it*?

Miss Cole: ² .... half past four.

Anita: When's *Peter Pan*?

Miss Cole: ³ .... quarter to six.

Tony: What about *Seven Years*?

Miss Cole: It's ⁴ .... Thursday at
quarter ⁵ .... five.

Anita: *Seven Years* is a boys' film.
When ⁶ .... *Beautiful World*?

Score ____ /5

6 Match the words.

1 About   a) late!
2 We're   b) up!
3 Don't   c) hopeless.
4 It's only   d) be silly!
5 Hurry   e) a hundred.
6 You're   f) right.
7 He's   g) a joke.

| 1 | e | 2 | | 3 | | 4 | |

| 5 | | 6 | | 7 | |

Score ____ /6

Check your score

TOTAL ____ /40

Brilliant! (30–40)
Good! (20–29)
OK (10–19)

Go to page 84 to see Puzzle Story 2 and to page 90 for the play.

21 Help! I can't swim!

Free time

1 Join the words to make free time activities.

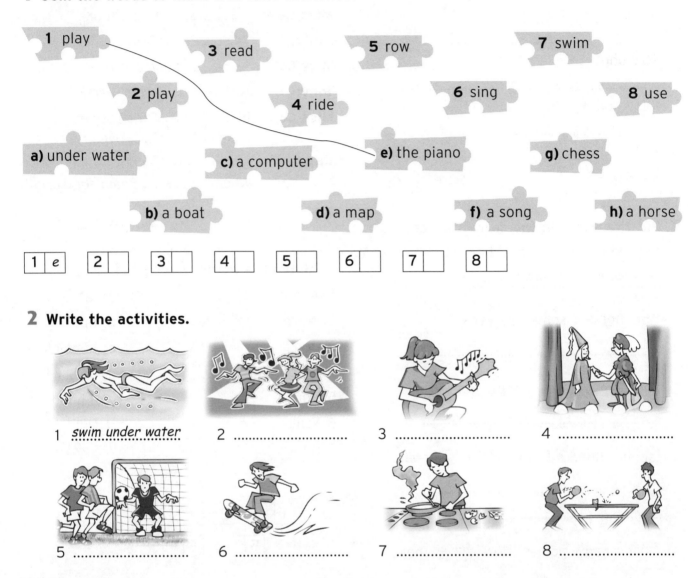

1 play	3 read	5 row	7 swim
2 play	4 ride	6 sing	8 use

a) under water   **c)** a computer   **e)** the piano   **g)** chess

b) a boat   **d)** a map   **f)** a song   **h)** a horse

1	e	2		3		4		5		6		7		8	

2 Write the activities.

1 *swim under water*
2 ....
3 ....
4 ....

5 ....
6 ....
7 ....
8 ....

can/can't

3 Write sentences using *can* or *can't*.

1 *I can swim under water.*
(I/swim under water/✓)

2 *We can't use a computer.*
(we/use a computer/✗)

3 ....
(you/make an omelette/✓)

4 ....
(they/play the piano/✓)

5 ....
(he/skateboard/✗)

6 ....
(we/row a boat/✓)

7 ....
(I/play table tennis/✗)

8 ....
(she/play chess/✓)

9 ....
(you/ride a horse/✗)

4 Complete the sentences using *can* or *can't*.

1 Frank *can't* skateboard.

2 Jenny and Steve ....

3 Rob ....

4 Amanda and Emily ....

5 Paula and Simon ....

6 Lynn ....

Questions with *can*

5 Look at Exercise 4 again. Write questions and short answers.

1 *Can Frank skateboard? No, he can't.*

2 ....
....

3 ....

4 ....
....

5 ....
....

6 ....

6 Ask Paula questions.

		✓	✗
Paula		play table tennis	play the guitar
Peter (Paula's brother)		use a computer	ride a horse

1 **You:** *Can you play the guitar?* .... (you)
   Paula: No, I can't.

2 **You:** .... (brother)
   Paula: Yes, he can.

3 **You:** .... (you)
   Paula: Yes, I can.

4 **You:** .... (brother)
   Paula: No, he can't.

7 Complete the conversation.

> You can't   Can you (✗ 2)   I can (✗ 2)
> You can   I can't

Sam: What's that?

Elliot: It's a photo of my uncle's horse.

Sam: [1] *Can you* ride a horse?

Elliot: Yes, [2] ....

Sam: You're very clever. [3] .... ride a horse and you can play the piano.

Elliot: [4] .... ride a horse?

Sam: No, [5] .... But [6] .... ride a cow.

Elliot: A cow! Don't be silly, Sam. [7] .... ride a cow.

Sam: It's only a joke!

22 Can I help you?

Drinks

1 Rearrange the letters to make drinks.

1 t h o l o t e c c h o a = *hot chocolate*
2 n i r a m e l e a t w r = ...
3 n a b n a a k k i s h e m l a = ...
4 g a r o e n i c e u j = ...
5 l o c a = ...
6 d e m a n l o e = ...
7 r a s t e r y w b r k a l e s h m i k = ...

Can I have ...?

2 Say what you want.

1 *Can I have a vanilla ice cream, please?*

2 ....

3 ....

4 ....

5 ....

6 ....

British money

3 Match the prices to the words.

1 £2.50   a) one pound twenty-five
2 £5.00   b) fifty pence
3 £1.25   c) five pounds
4 £3.70   d) six pounds ninety-nine
5 £6.99   e) two pounds fifty
6 50p   f) three pounds seventy

1	e		4	
2			5	
3			6	

How much ...?

4a **Look at the picture. Write questions and answers.**

1 (books) _How much are the books?_ _They're 50p._
2 (T-shirt) ....
3 (CDs) ....
4 (posters) ....

5 (camera) ....
6 (radio) ....
7 (watches) ....
8 (mobile) ....

4b **Complete the conversation. Use the phrases in the box.**

It's twelve ~~Can I~~ much are much is
No, thanks They're one pound twenty

A: Hello. [1] _Can I_ help you?

B: Yes, please. How [2] .... the mobile phone?

A: [3] .... pounds sixty.

B: And how [4] .... the CDs?

A: [5] .... each.

B: Oh! You've got an S Club Juniors CD!

A: It's not my CD. It's my sister's CD. It's only thirty pence.

B: [6] .... · I don't like S Club Juniors! It's kids' music!

Listening

5 (10) **Listen. Complete the conversation.**

Lucy: [1] _Can we have an ice cream_, please, Dad?

Mr Barr: Sure.

Lucy: [2] ....?

Mr Barr: They've got strawberry, banana, vanilla and chocolate. Jodie?

Jodie: [3] .... a chocolate ice cream, please?

Lucy: Me too, please, Dad.

Rob: Strawberry for me, please.

Man: [4] ....?

Mr Barr: Yes, please. [5] ....
.... ?

Man: They're £1.75. The double cones are £3.60.

Mr Barr: OK. Two single chocolate cones and one strawberry, please.

Kim: [6] .... a double cone with strawberry, vanilla and chocolate, please?

45

23 Don't move!

The body

1 **Find 14 words in the puzzle.**

A	S	D	T	O	H	A	P
L	T	H	U	M	B	R	S
M	I	B	S	I	G	M	O
O	W	P	H	A	N	D	T
U	S	T	O	M	A	C	H
T	A	D	U	P	M	E	E
H	M	E	L	O	F	B	A
I	F	L	D	M	I	S	D
N	O	S	E	K	N	A	H
S	O	H	R	I	G	T	L
P	T	O	E	A	E	Y	E
K	N	E	E	P	R	H	G

2 **Match the words with the picture.**

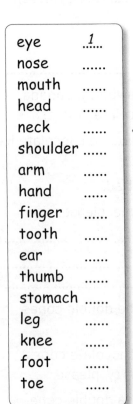

eye _1_
nose ......
mouth ......
head ......
neck ......
shoulder ......
arm ......
hand ......
finger ......
tooth ......
ear ......
thumb ......
stomach ......
leg ......
knee ......
foot ......
toe ......

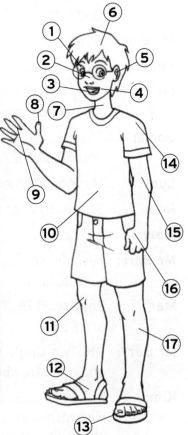

Verbs

3 **Write the verbs.**

close   draw   hold up   ~~jump~~   open
point   sit down   stand up

1 _jump_ ....

2 ....

3 ....

4 ....

5 ....

6 ....

7 ....

8 ....

4 **Write negative sentences for pictures in Exercise 3.**

3 _Don't open the door._ ....

6 ....

2 ....

5 ....

1 ....

Action + parts of the body

5 Find the stickers.

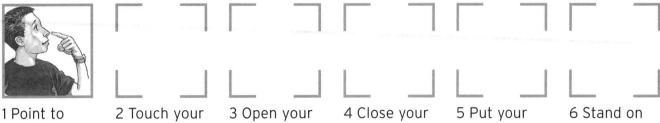

1 Point to your nose.
2 Touch your shoulder.
3 Open your mouth.
4 Close your eyes.
5 Put your hands on your knees.
6 Stand on one leg.

Listening

6 🎧 11 **Listen. Complete the conversation.**

> be   come   ~~feel~~   Go   move
> open   Point   see
> Show   Stand

Jodie: Lucy!

Lucy: What's the matter?

Jodie: There's something on the back of my neck. I can ¹ *feel* it.

Lucy: ² .... me. ³ .... up and ⁴ .... here.

Jodie: What is it?

Lucy: Where? I can't ⁵ .... ⁶ .... to it!

Jodie: There! It's on my back now.

Lucy: Don't ⁷ ....

Jodie: Now it's on my leg!

Lucy: Don't ⁸ .... silly! It's only a bumblebee!

Jodie: Ooh! ⁹ .... away, bumblebee!

Lucy: Don't ¹⁰ .... your mouth, Jodie! It's on your nose!

Song

Stand Still and Don't Smile

7 🎧 12 **Listen. Choose the correct word.**

Can you stand still on your left leg?
Can you stand still on your right leg?
Can you hold your left ¹ *hand / foot / knee* with your right hand?
Can you keep a straight face and not smile?

Stand still and don't smile, stand still and don't smile,
Stand still and don't smile, now relax and ² *jump / sit / stand* up straight.

Can you touch your left ³ *eye / knee / ear* with your right thumb?
Can you touch your right knee with your left thumb?
Can you touch both ⁴ *feet / eyes / legs* with both hands?
Can you keep a straight face and not smile?

Stand still and don't smile, stand still and don't smile,
Stand still and don't smile, now relax and stand up straight.

Go to page 95 to see the completed song.

47

1 Match the questions to the answers.

1 ☐ 2 ☐ 3 ☐

New words

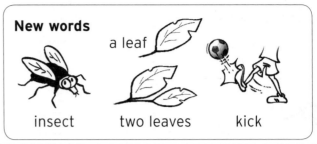

insect   two leaves   kick

Mr Clever Cat's Question and Answer Page

1 Can young children speak different languages?

2 Can giraffes swim?

3 Can some plants catch insects?

Mamma! Dad!

A Yes, they can. The Venus Fly Trap can catch insects. It's got two big leaves and it can close the leaves and catch the insect. This is a Venus Fly Trap. It's from the jungle in South America. It's a beautiful plant. It's green and red and it can catch five insects in one day.

B Yes, they can. Children can understand two or three languages at the same time. Mariella is three. Her Italian mother talks to her in Italian and her English father talks to her in English. Mariella can answer them in both languages. It isn't a problem for her.

C No, they can't. Giraffes can run very fast and kick other animals, but they can't swim. Boris is a giraffe in Bristol Zoo. He is very tall (about 5.5 metres) and his neck measures 2 metres. Baby giraffes are about 180 centimetres tall.

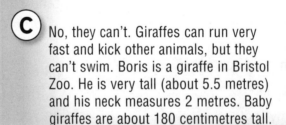

2 Answer the questions.

1 Can some plants catch insects? *Yes, they can.* ....

2 Where is the Venus Fly Trap from? ....

3 Can young children speak different languages? ....

4 Can Mariella speak English? ....

5 Can giraffes run fast? ....

6 How long is Boris's neck? ....

3 🎧 **⟨13⟩ Listen to Danny and Mr Clever Cat. Choose the correct word.**

1 Computers *can* / *can't* play chess.

2 Computers now are fast and *clever* / *complicated*.

3 *Deep Blue* is a famous *computer* / *chess player*.

4 Gary Kasparov is a famous *scientist* / *chess player*.

5 Computers *can* / *can't* play football.

STUDY TIP!
When you learn new words, it is sometimes useful to write the words in a sentence.

4 Write these new words in sentences.

(leaves   heavy   insect)

The leaves on the tree are beautiful.
....

5 Look at your answers to Exercise 3. Write about *Deep Blue* in your notebook. Use the prompts.

What is *Deep Blue*? What can it do?

(famous computer/clever/very well/Gary Kasparov/play football)

'Deep Blue' is a famous computer. It …
....

Cartoon Time: Future World
6 Complete the conversation. Use the words in the box.

(Can   help   rude   point   Sure   ~~there~~   only)

Mixi:	Hey, Robomo, look who's over ¹*there*! It's my teacher, Mrs Klix.
Robomo:	Don't ² .... It's rude.
Girl:	Can I ³ .... you?

Mixi: ⁴ .... I have a coffee, please?
Girl: ⁵ ....· With milk?
Mixi: Yes, please.
Girl: That's £18, please.
Mixi: Oh no! I've ⁶ .... got £17!

Robomo: Look, there's £1 on the floor.
Mixi: Where?
Robomo: There.
Mixi and Zar: Don't point! It's ⁷ ....!

25 Revision

1 Put the letters in the correct order.

1 orw a abot = *row a boat* ....
2 aypl eht oainp = ...
3 kema na eoelemtt = ...
4 iedr a roesh = ...
5 nsgi a nsog = ...
6 daer a pam = ...

Score ___ /5

2 Look at the chart. Write the sentences and questions.

	Peter	Paula	Liz and Billy
play chess	✗	✓	?
make an omelette	?	✗	✗
swim under water	✓	?	✓

1 *Peter can swim under water.* ....
   (Peter/swim under water)

2 *Can Liz and Billy play chess?* ....
   (Liz and Billy/play chess)

3 ....
   (Paula/make an omelette)

4 ....
   (Peter/make an omelette)

5 ....
   ....
   (Liz and Billy/swim under water)

6 ....
   ....
   (Liz and Billy/make an omelette)

7 ....
   ....
   (Paula/swim under water)

Score ___ /5

3 Complete the conversations.

Girl: Hi. Can I help you?
Liz: Yes, please. [1] *Have*.. you got any milkshakes?
Girl: Yes, they're £1.50.
Liz: [2] .... I have a milkshake and an ice [3] ...., please?

Boy: Hello. Can I help you?
Paula: How much is a [4] .... chocolate?
Boy: It's 75p.
Paula: Oh no! I've only [5] .... 50p.

Billy: Can I have a [6] .... water, please?
Peter: And can I have an orange [7] ...., please?
Girl: Sure. That's £2.50, please.

Score ___ /6

4 Complete the conversation.

have   Don't   rude   sure
~~help~~   there   much

Girl: Hello. Can I [1] *help*.. you?
Liz: Yes, please. How [2] .... are the milkshakes?
Girl: They're £1.10.
Liz: Can I [3] .... two, please?
Girl: Yes, [4] ....·
Peter: Hey, Liz. Look who's [5] ....!
Paula: Don't point, Peter. It's [6] ....·
Peter: But it's Billy – your boyfriend.
Paula: Billy's not my boyfriend!
Peter: Is he your husband?
Liz: Come on, Peter. [7] .... be silly.

Score ___ /6

5 Label Robogirl.

1 hand ....

2 ....

3 ....

4 ....

5 ....

6 ....

7 ....

6 Write sentences with *please* or *don't*.

1 Please close the window.

2 Don't sit down!

3 ....
....

4 ....
....

5 ....
....

6 ....
....

7 Write questions and answers.

1 A: How much is the boat?

   B: It's £3.40.

2 A: How much are the CDs?

   B: They're 80p each.

3 A: ....
   ....

   B: ....

4 A: ....
   ....

   B: ....

5 A: ....
   ....

   B: ....

6 A: ....
   ....

   B: ....

26 Do you like this T-shirt?

Clothes

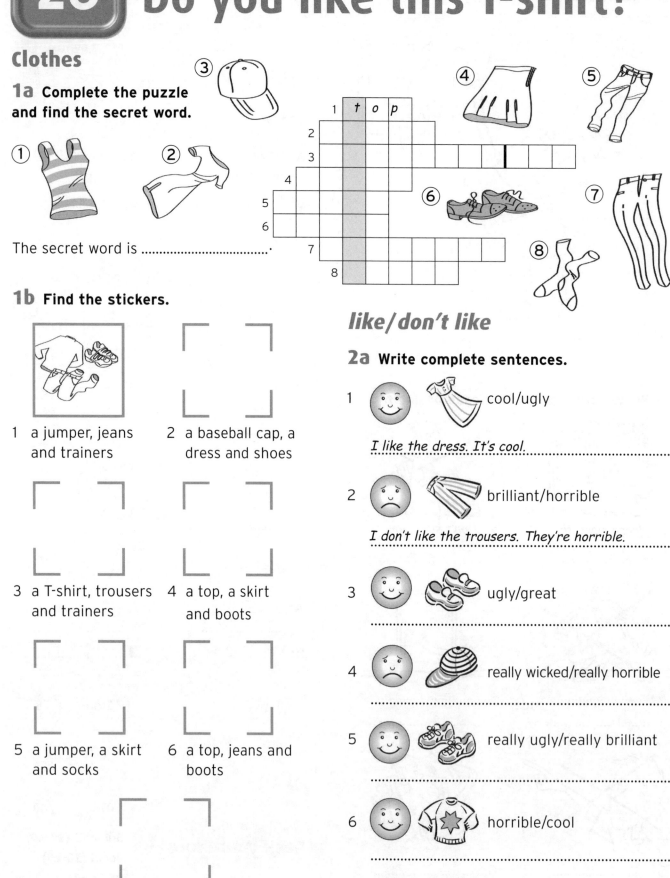

1a Complete the puzzle and find the secret word.

	1	t	o	p					
2									
3									
4									
5									
6									
7									
8									

The secret word is ....

1b Find the stickers.

1 a jumper, jeans and trainers
2 a baseball cap, a dress and shoes

3 a T-shirt, trousers and trainers
4 a top, a skirt and boots

5 a jumper, a skirt and socks
6 a top, jeans and boots

7 a T-shirt, trousers and shoes

like/don't like

2a Write complete sentences.

1 cool/ugly

I like the dress. It's cool.

2 brilliant/horrible

I don't like the trousers. They're horrible.

3 ugly/great

....

4 really wicked/really horrible

....

5 really ugly/really brilliant

....

6 horrible/cool

....

7 really wicked/really ugly

....

2b Write questions and answers.

1 **Billy:** *Do you like his baseball cap?*

(baseball cap)

Liz: *Yes, I do.*   (✓)

2 **Billy:** *Do you like his trainers?*

(trainers)

Liz: *No, I don't.*   (✗)

3 **Billy:** ....

(T-shirt)

Liz: ....   (✓)

4 **Billy:** ....

(jeans)

Liz: ....   (✗)

5 **Billy:** ....

(socks)

Liz: ....   (✓)

6 **Billy:** ....

(top)

Liz: ....   (✗)

me, you, him, her, it, us, them

3a Match a word in A to a word in B. Write the pairs of words in C.

Ⓐ

> + you
> he she it
> we they

Ⓑ

> her you
> them ~~me~~ us
> him it

Ⓒ

I – *me*
.... – ....
.... – ....
.... – ....
.... – ....
.... – ....
.... – ....
.... – ....

3b Replace the underlined words with the words in the box.

> he ~~him~~ him she her it we us they ~~they~~ them

1 <u>Mike and Carla</u> like <u>Paul</u>.

They like *him.*

2 I like <u>your jeans</u>.

I like ....·

3 <u>Tina and Gary</u> don't like <u>Sally</u>.

.... don't like ....·

4 <u>Paul and I</u> like <u>David</u>.

.... like ....·

5 <u>Sue</u> doesn't like <u>Paul and me</u>.

.... doesn't like ....·

6 <u>Mark</u> likes me.

.... likes me.

7 I like <u>your top</u>.

I like ....·

27 They sleep in caves.

Wild animals

1 Complete the words with a letter. Use the new letters to make another animal.

1 CROCODI L E

2 MONK _ Y

3 LI _ N

4 CHIM _ ANZEE

5 K _ NGAROO

6 TIGE _

7 PAN _ A

The secret animal is ....

2 Label the pictures.

monkey ....

....

....

....

....

....

....

Present simple

3 Join words from A, B and C to make sentences.

A	B	C
Tigers Rabbits	eat don't eat climb don't climb live don't live	in the jungle plants and fruit trees

1 *Tigers don't eat plants and fruit.*

2 ....

3 ....

4 ....

5 ....

6 ....

4 Complete the sentences with the verbs in brackets.

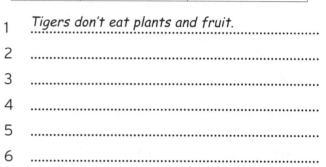

Pandas [1] *don't live* (✗ live) in the jungle.

They [2] .... (✓ live) in the mountains.

They [3] .... (✓ climb) trees but they

[4] .... (✗ run) fast.

They [5] .... (✗ eat) meat. They

[6] .... (✓ eat) plants.

5 Look at the pictures. Write sentences.

> eat plants
> ~~climb trees~~
> swing from tree to tree
> hunt at night
> ~~sleep at night~~
> run fast

1 ✓ _Horses sleep at night._

2 ✗ _Cows don't climb trees._

3 ✗ ....

4 ✓ ....

5 ✗ ....

6 ✓ ....

Questions with Present simple

6 Rearrange the words to make questions. Write short answers.

1 | tigers | meat | do | eat | ? | (✓)

Do tigers eat meat?   _Yes, they do._

2 | eat | dogs | fruit | do | ? | (✗)

....

3 | night | cats | sleep | do | at | ? | (✗)

....

4 | the | giraffes | in | do | live | jungle | ? | (✓)

....

5 | trees | monkeys | climb | do | ? | (✓)

....

6 | at | elephants | hunt | do | night | ? | (✗)

....

7 Look at the pictures. Write questions and answers.

1 **A:** _Do crocodiles eat fruit?_ .... (eat fruit)
   B: _No, they don't._ .... (✗)

2 **A:** .... (run fast)
   B: .... (✗)

3 **A:** .... (sleep in the day)
   B: .... (✓)

4 **A:** .... (climb trees)
   B: .... (✗)

5 **A:** .... (live to 70)
   B: .... (✓)

28 She has lessons at the studio.

Daily routine

1 Label the pictures.

play sports   ~~get up~~   watch TV
go to school   play computer games
do homework

1 *get up* ....   2 ....

3 ....   4 ....

5 ....   6 ....

2 Match the words to the times.

watch TV   go to school   go to bed
have lunch   finish school   ~~get up~~

1 **07:30**   *get up* ....
2 **08:30**   ....
3 **12:30**   ....
4 **15:30**   ....
5 **20:30**   ....
6 **21:30**   ....

Present simple

3 Write sentences with *he* or *she*.

1 They have breakfast at half past seven.
He *has breakfast at half past seven.* ....

2 We don't play sports.
She ....

3 I go to school at eight o'clock.
He ....

4 You don't play computer games.
He ....

5 I get up at seven o'clock.
She ....

6 We go to bed at quarter past nine.
He ....

7 They watch TV all day.
He ....

8 We have dinner at half past seven.
She ....

4 Write negative sentences.

1 She has dinner at school.
She doesn't have dinner at school. ....

2 My dog plays sport in the afternoon.
....

3 Peter watches TV in the morning.
....

4 Sheila gets up at 11.
....

5 Jim does homework in the morning.
....

6 My cat plays computer games.
....

5 Complete the sentences about Fran Fast and Simon Slow.

1 Fran *gets up* at half past five.

2 Simon *doesn't get up* at half past five.

3 Fran .... at six o'clock.

4 Simon .... at half past eleven.

5 Fran .... computer games.

6 Simon .... sports.

7 Fran .... at half past ten.

8 Simon .... at half past ten.

Questions with *does*

6 Write questions and answers.

1 **A:** *Does Fran get up at half past five?* ....
(Fran/get up at half past five)
B: *Yes, she does.*

2 **A:** *Does Simon get up at half past five?* ....
(Simon/get up at half past five)
B: *No, he doesn't.*

3 **A:** ....
(Fran/have breakfast at half past eleven)
B: ....

4 **A:** ....
(Simon/have breakfast at half past eleven)
B: ....

5 **A:** ....
(Fran/play sports)
B: ....

6 **A:** ....
(Simon/play sports)
B: ....

7 **A:** ....
(Fran/go to bed at half past ten)
B: ....

8 **A:** ....
(Simon/go to bed at half past ten)
B: ....

7 Read Liz's poem. Answer the questions.

Billy is twelve and he's very cool,
He gets up at eight and he goes to school.
When he finishes school at half past
*   three,*
He does his homework and watches TV.
On Saturday morning at half past ten,
He plays football in the garden with his
*   friend Ben.*
On Sunday afternoon at quarter to three,
He goes to the cinema with Paula and me!

1 What time does Billy get up?
He gets up at eight.
....

2 What does he do at half past three?
....

3 What does he do on Saturday morning?
....

4 Where does he play football?
....

5 Where does he go on Sunday afternoon?
....

6 What time does he go to the cinema?
....

29 Skills practice

Reading

1 Read Melanie's letter. Complete the sentences.

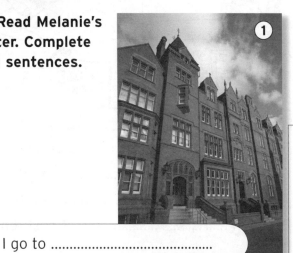

> I go to ....

> I .... in the school ....

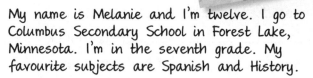

> On Thursday I ....

Dear penfriend

My name is Melanie and I'm twelve. I go to Columbus Secondary School in Forest Lake, Minnesota. I'm in the seventh grade. My favourite subjects are Spanish and History.

I start school at 8 and I have six lessons a day. I have lunch at 12 in the school cafeteria. After lunch there is a study period from 12.30 to 1.30 and I do my homework then. Lessons start again at 1.45. I finish at 3.00. On Wednesday after school I play in the school band and on Thursday I do basketball.

What about you? Where do you go to school? What are your favourite subjects? What time do you start and finish school? What do you do in the afternoon? Do you like sports? I want to know!

Write soon!

Melanie

2 Complete the chart.

	Melanie
1 How old?	....
2 Start school	....
3 Number of lessons	....
4 Favourite subjects	....
5 Have lunch	....
6 Finish school	....
7 Do homework	....
8 After school activities	....

Writing

STUDY TIP!

Use capital letters for:
• days of the week and months of the year,
• languages and nationalities,
• school subjects.

3 Write the sentences using capital letters for the correct words.

1 we can go to london on tuesday.

....

2 we study maths on thursday and french on friday.

....

3 her favourite day is wednesday because there's science in the morning.

....

4 i can speak italian and english.

....

4 Read about Agnes, Melanie's French friend. Answer the questions.

Name:	Agnes
Age:	13
School week:	Monday-Friday all day, Saturday morning
School:	from 8 a.m. to 5 p.m.
Lunch time:	12–2 p.m. (goes home)
Favourite lessons:	Music, English

1 Where is Agnes from? ....

2 Does she go to school on Saturday?

....

3 Where does she have lunch?

....

4 What time does school finish?

....

5 What are her favourite lessons?

....

5 Write a paragraph about Agnes. Use the information in Exercise 4.

Agnes is 13 and she's from France. She goes to school ...

Cartoon Time: Future World

6 Complete the conversation.
Use the words in the box.

> ugly alone ~~are~~ them really
> away beautiful

Zar: Hi, Mixi. What ¹ *are* they?
Mixi: They are my new fish, Imple, Dimple and Simple. Do you like ² ....?

Zar: Wow! They're ³ .... horrible.
Mixi: No, they're not. They're ⁴ .... And they're very clever.
Zar: Don't be silly, Mixi. Fish aren't clever.

Imple: Wow! He's really ⁵ ....
Dimple: Yes. Go ⁶ ...., boy.
Simple: Leave us ⁷ ....!

30 Revision

Billy

Peter

Paula

1 What are the clothes?

Billy: a *T-shirt,* ....
.... and
....

Paula: a ....,
.... and
....

Peter: a ....,
.... and
....

Score ___ /8

2 Circle the correct words.

1   I don't like his boots.
    They / *Them* / *Their* are ugly.

2   She's really cool.
    I like *she* / *her* / *she's*.

3   My cousin lives with *we* / *us* / *our*
    in the school holidays.

4   I like your brother.
    What's *he* / *him* / *his* name?

5   Does Shelly like *I* / *me* / *my*?

6   My brother goes to Park Road School.
    He / *His* / *Him* starts school at
    nine o'clock.

7   Your trousers are wicked.
    I like *they* / *them* / *their*.

Score ___ /6

3 Write sentences.

1   *Cows don't eat meat.*
    (cows/eat meat/✗)

2   *Do horses run fast?*
    (horses/run fast/?)

3   *Chickens sleep at night.*
    (chickens/sleep at night/✓)

4   ....
    (tigers/eat fruit/✗)

5   ....
    ....
    (chimpanzees/swing from tree to tree/✓)

6   ....
    (giraffes/eat meat/?)

7   ....
    (dogs/like people/✓)

8   ....
    (dogs/like cats/✗)

9   ....
    ....
    (elephants/live in the jungle/?)

Score ___ /6

4 Look at the pictures. Write questions and answers about Paula.

1 *What time does she have breakfast?*
....
(what time/she/have breakfast)
She has breakfast at eight o'clock.
....

2 ....
(what/she/have for breakfast)
....

3 ....
(what time/she/start school)
....

4 ....
(where/she/go to school)
....

5 ....
(where/she/have lunch)
....

Score ____ /8

5 Complete the conversation.

> Have   play   live   ~~I'm~~
> Do   is   don't

A: Let's play a game.

B: What game?

A: OK, I'm a famous person. Who am I?

B: Are you a woman?

A: No, ¹ *I'm* not.

B: ² .... you got a wife?

A: Yes, I have. My wife ³ .... a singer.

B: ⁴ .... you play sports?

A: Yes, I do. But I ⁵ .... play basketball or cricket.

B: Do you ⁶ .... tennis?

A: No, I don't. I play football.

B: Do you ⁷ .... in Italy?

A: No, I don't.

B: Are you David Beckham?

A: Yes, I am. Well done! Your turn.

Score ____ /6

6 Find six school subjects.

E	N	G	L	I	S	H
W	V	A	U	L	P	I
A	M	G	E	S	A	S
A	Q	B	A	M	N	T
D	O	F	R	G	I	O
S	M	A	T	H	S	R
F	R	E	N	C	H	Y

1 *English*
2 ....
3 ....
4 ....
5 ....
6 ....
7 ....

Score ____ /6

TOTAL ____ /40

Check your score

Brilliant! (30–40)
Good! (20–29)
OK (10–19)

Go to page 86 to see Puzzle Story 3.

31 I often read in bed.

Everyday activities (1)

1 Match the words to make everyday activities.

1	watch	a)	to sleep
2	read	b)	cards
3	have	c)	to music
4	meet	d)	in bed
5	go	e)	home
6	walk	f)	a snack
7	play	g)	a DVD
8	listen	h)	friends

1	*g*	2		3		4		5		6		7		8	

2 Look at the pictures. Complete the sentences about Happy Harry.

> play cards ~~gets up~~ listens to music   meets friends
> goes to bed   watches a DVD

On Saturday, Harry ¹ *gets up* at eight o'clock.
Then he ² .... in his bedroom. After
lunch, he ³ .... and they
⁴ ....· In the evening, he ⁵ ....
................· About nine o'clock, Happy Harry
⁶ ....·

Adverbs of frequency

3 Put the words in brackets in the correct place.

1   Harry is late for school.
    (never)
    Harry is never late for school.
    ....

2   Sally and Mike meet friends
    on Sunday.   (often)
    ....
    ....

3   Harry is happy.   (always)
    ....
    ....

4   I play football with Harry on
    Saturdays.   (sometimes)
    ....
    ....

5   You are hungry.   (always)
    ....
    ....

6   Mark plays games on his
    computer in the evening.
    (never)
    ....
    ....

7   Liz reads in bed.   (often)
    ....
    ....

8   Peter is bored in class.
    (sometimes)
    ....
    ....

9   We go to bed at nine o'clock.
    (usually)
    ....
    ....

How often ...?

4 Write questions and answers.

1 How often (you/visit) your grandparents at the weekend?
How often do you visit your grandparents at the weekend?
I often visit my grandparents at the weekend.

2 How often (you/be) late for school?
....
....

3 How often (you/play) computer games after school?
....
....

4 How often (you/walk) to school?
....
....

5 How often (you/be) tired in the evening?
....
....

5 Complete the conversation.

Elliot: [1] *What time do you go* (What time/you/go) to bed, Hannah?

Hannah: [2] *I usually go at half past nine* (usually/half past nine). What about you?

Elliot: [3] .... (usually/nine o'clock), but if [4] .... (there/be) a good film on TV, [5] .... (sometimes/watch) it and then [6] .... (go) to bed late.

Hannah: [7] .... (you/be/tired) in the mornings?

Elliot: [8] .... (usually/be/OK). But [9] .... (sometimes/ fall asleep) in lessons! But the teachers [10] .... (never/see)! How often [11] .... (you/go to bed/late)?

Hannah: [12] .... (never). [13] .... (always/be/tired) at nine o'clock!

6 Look at the pictures. Write questions and answers.

often late
09:10
SCHOOL

1 **You:** *How often are you late for school?*

Peter: *I'm often late for school.*

sometimes play

2 **You:** ....
....

Peter: ....
....

always happy

3 **You:** ....
....

Peter: ....
....

never read

4 **You:** ....
....

Peter: ....
....

32 I'm walking to the London Eye.

Everyday activities (2)

1 **Match the words to make everyday activities.**

1 do —————— a) a sandwich
2 listen to b) a photo
3 take c) a shower
4 write d) homework
5 make e) the radio
6 have f) an email

| 1 | d | 2 | | 3 | | 4 | | 5 | | 6 | |

2 **Find the stickers.**

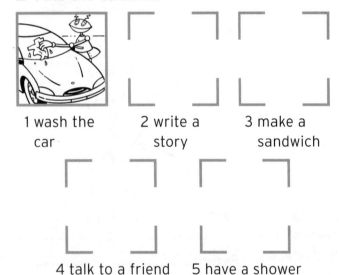

1 wash the car   2 write a story   3 make a sandwich

4 talk to a friend   5 have a shower

The -ing form

3 **Change the verbs to the -ing form.**

1 talk → _talking_   6 do → ....
2 write → .... 7 take → ....
3 sit → .... 8 make → ....
4 listen → .... 9 wash → ....
5 have → .... 10 study → ....

He's/She's + -ing

4 **Look at the picture. Write what the people are doing.**

> drink a milkshake
> eat a sandwich   ~~listen to music~~
> read a book   sleep   talk to Elliot

1 Amy _'s listening to music_ and ....
....
2 Sam ....
....
3 Hannah ....
....
4 Rusty ....
....
5 Elliot ....
....

5 Look at the picture in Exercise 4 again. Write questions and short answers.

1 Hannah/eat a pizza?
Is Hannah eating a pizza? No, she isn't.

2 Elliot/listen to Hannah?
....

3 Amy/drink a milkshake?
....

4 Sam/read a book?
....

5 Elliot/sleep?
....

6 Write negative sentences about the picture in Exercise 4.

1 Amy *isn't talking to Hannah.*
2 Sam ....
3 Hannah ....
4 Elliot ....
5 Rusty ....

Listening

7 🎧 **Listen. Complete the conversations.**

Jodie: Hello. 937 2261.
Lucy: Hello. It's me, Lucy.
Jodie: Hi, Lucy. What are you [1] *doing?* Are you doing your [2] ....?
Lucy: No, I'm not. Don't be daft, Jodie! I don't do homework on [3] ....!
I'm [4] .... to the London Eye with Rob and Amber.
Jodie: Lucky you! I'm so [5] ....
Lucy: What are you doing?
Jodie: I'm making a [6] .... in the kitchen.
Rob: Jodie, is Leo watching the [7] ....?
Jodie: Yes, he is.
Rob: Who's [8] ....?
Jodie: Arsenal. Sorry!

8 Complete the conversation about the people in Exercise 4.

Hannah: Hi, Mum.
Mum: Hello, Hannah. What [1] *are you doing* (you/do)?
Hannah: I [2] .... (sit) at a café.
Mum: [3] .... (you/eat) something?
Hannah: [4] .... · Elliot [5] .... (eat) a sandwich, and Amy [6] .... (have) a drink, but I'm not hungry.
Mum: What [7] .... (Amy/drink)?
Hannah: A milkshake.
Mum: Is Sam there?
Hannah: Yes, he is.
Mum: What [8] .... (he/do)?
Hannah: [9] ....
Mum: [10] .... (Rusty/sleep)?
Hannah: [11] ....

 **What's the weather like?**

The weather

1 Find seven weather words.

F	S	T	F	C	P
Y	U	C	O	L	D
H	N	S	G	O	W
O	N	A	G	U	A
T	Y	K	Y	D	R
W	I	N	D	Y	M

1 *sunny* ....
2 ....
3 ....
4 ....
5 ....
6 ....
7 ....

2 What's the weather like? Write the sentences under the pictures.

It's windy.   ~~It's hot.~~   It's raining.   It's cold.   The sun is shining.   It's snowing.

(1)

It's hot. ....

....

(2)

....

....

(3)

....

....

3 Match the questions to the answers.

1 Where are you?
2 What are you doing at the moment?
3 What's the weather like?
4 Who are you staying with?
5 What are you wearing?
6 Where are your parents?

a) Our aunt and uncle.
b) We're having lunch.
c) They're shopping in town.
d) We're in Paris.
e) It's cold and windy.
f) Boots, trousers and a big jumper.

1	d	2		3		4		5		6	

Present continuous

4 **Complete the sentences.**

~~do~~   have   play   listen to   wear

1 **Sam and Jess:**
   We're doing homework.

2 **Hannah and Elliot:**
   .... tennis.
   ....
   shorts.

3 **Amy and Scott:**
   .... lunch.
   ....
   music.

5 **Look at the pictures in Exercise 4 again. Write conversations.**

1 **A:** *Are Sam and Jess doing homework?*
   ....
   (Sam and Jess/do homework)
   B: *Yes, they are.*
   ....

2 **A:** ....
   (Sam and Jess/swim in the pool)
   B: ....

3 **A:** ....
   (Hannah and Elliot/shop in town)
   B: ....

4 **A:** ....
   (Hannah and Elliot/play tennis)
   B: ....

5 **A:** ....
   (Amy and Scott/listen to music)
   B: ....

6 **A:** ....
   (Amy and Scott/read magazines)
   B: ....

Song
The Mouse Party

6 (15) **Listen. Complete the song.**

Dad is in the [1] ...., he's learning
   how to [2] ....
Mum is in the [3] ....,
   she's reading a good [4] ....
But when the house is empty,
   the mice begin to play,
They eat [5] .... and
   watch TV and sing their songs all
   day.

Grandad's in the [6] ....,
   he's playing cards with Jack.
Grandma's in the [7] ....,
   she's having a big snack.
But when the house is empty,
   the mice begin again.
They drink [8] ...., play
   music loud and turn it up to ten!

The [9] .... is in the garden
   but the cat is in the [10] ....,
He's looking for a meal to eat,
   he's looking for a [11] ....
When the cat is hungry, the mice all
   stay away,
They don't get up and don't sing
   songs and don't go out all day!

Go to page 95 to see the completed song.

34 Skills practice

1 Read the texts. Complete the sentences under the pictures.

Yorkshire
Cornwall

1 Jeremy and his .... on the beach in ....·

TEXT 1: JEREMY

For my summer holiday, I always go to Cornwall, in southwest England with my family. In this photo, I'm with my brother. We're learning how to surf. The climate in Cornwall is very good. It's quite warm in winter, and in the summer it can be very hot. On holiday, I usually get up about nine o'clock and go to the beach with my brother. We listen to music, swim or surf. Then we have lunch with our parents. I love my summer holiday!

TEXT 2: ELEANOR

For my summer holiday, I usually go to our cottage in Yorkshire with my mum and brother. Yorkshire is in the north of England. In this photo, I'm walking in the country with my cousin. On holiday we walk a lot and we sometimes ride horses. In the photo, the sun isn't shining but it's nice and warm. It isn't always warm in Yorkshire in the summer! There's a lot of rain and it can be foggy, too. In the winter there's a lot of snow. But it's a very beautiful place.

2 Eleanor with her .... in ....·

2 Write answers.

1 Where is Cornwall? *It's in southwest England.* ....

2 What are Jeremy and his brother doing in the photo? ....

3 Does Cornwall have a warm climate? ....

4 What time does Jeremy get up on holiday? ....

5 Where do Eleanor and her family stay in Yorkshire? ....

6 What two sports does Eleanor do on holiday? ....

7 Is Yorkshire warm in the winter? ....

8 Does Eleanor like Yorkshire? ....

Portfolio

STUDY TIP!

When you want to find new words in a dictionary, it's much quicker if you know the alphabet well.

3 Write these words in alphabetical order as fast as you can.

shirt swim Spain summer sleep
sunny sister salad

4 Draw a picture or find a photo of you on holiday. Then answer the questions.

1 Where are you in the picture?
....

2 Who are you with?
....

3 What are you doing?
....

4 What is the weather like?
....

5 Do you always go there in the summer?
....

6 On holiday, what do you usually do in the mornings/the afternoons/the evenings?
....

5 Write a letter to a friend about your holiday. Describe the weather.

Dear...

In this picture I'm... ....

Cartoon Time: Future World

6 Complete the conversation. Use the words in the box.

bed late good ~~Double~~ daft It's

Zar: Hello? [1] *Double.* seven, nine, five, six.
Mixi: Hi, Zar. [2] .... Mixi. What are you doing?
Zar: I'm writing a story in [3] ....·

Mixi: Why are you writing a story?
Zar: Because I'm [4] .... at stories.
Mixi: But we're [5] .... for school. It's half past eight.

Zar: Don't be [6] ....·' Mixi. It's Saturday.
Mixi: Oh dear.

35 Revision

1 Match the words to the pictures.

| 1 | c | 2 | | 3 | | 4 | | 5 | | 6 | |

1 play football
2 be bored
3 read in bed
4 listen to music
5 be late for school
6 be hungry

Score ___ /5

2 Make questions and answers.

1 **A:** *How often do you play football?*
   (you/play football?)
   B: *I never play football.*
   (I/never)

2 **A:** *How often is he bored on Sundays?*
   (he/bored on Sundays?)
   B: *He's sometimes bored on Sundays.*
   (he/sometimes)

3 **A:** ....
   (you/listen to music?)
   B: ....
   (I/often)

4 **A:** ....
   (she/be late for school?)
   B: ....
   (she/never)

5 **A:** ....
   (they/be hungry?)
   B: ....
   (they/always)

6 **A:** ....
   (he/read in bed?)
   B: ....
   (he/usually)

Score ___ /8

3 Complete the phrases.

take   do   wash   talk   write
make   have

1 *write*.. an email
2 .... my homework
3 .... a photo
4 .... to a friend
5 .... a sandwich
6 .... the car
7 .... a shower

Score ___ /6

4 What's the weather like? Write sentences.

1 *It's sunny.* ....

2 ....

3 ....

4 ....

5 ....

6 ....

Score ___ /5

5 Complete the conversation.

listen to the radio   do his homework
~~write an email~~   make a sandwich
talk to you   take a photo

Eva: Hi, Carrie. What are you doing?

Carrie: Hi, Eva. [1] *I'm writing an email.*

Eva: What's your dad doing?

Carrie: [2] ....

Eva: What's your mum doing?

Carrie: [3] ....

Eva: What's Nigel doing?

Carrie: [4] ....

Eva: What's Macy doing?

Carrie: [5] ....
And what are you doing?

Eva: [6] ....

Eva

Carrie

Dad

Mum

Nigel

Macy

Score ___ /5

6 Write the sentences in full to complete the email.

Send   Save   Insert File...   Priority   Options...

This mail message has been sent.

To... Vernon@rusmail.com

From Carla@myemail.net

Subject: Holiday

Arial   10   B I U

Hi, Vernon

How are you? We're in Spain at the moment. We're on holiday.
[1] *We are staying at our grandparents' house.*
....
(we/stay/our grandparents' house)
2
....
(they/be/on holiday/France)
3
....
(it/be/sunny and warm here)
4
....
(we/wear/T-shirts and shorts)
5
....
(what/you/do/moment?)
6
....
(what/weather/like/the UK?)

See you soon!
Love, Carla

7 Complete the telephone conversation.

double   good   bed
~~Hello~~   daft   It's   What's

A: [1] *Hello?*

B: Hi, Kate. [2] ....
Andy.

A: Hi, Andy. How are you?

B: I'm fine. I've got a new
mobile phone.

A: Great. [3] .... your
number?

B: It's three, [4] .... seven,
nine, one, two, eight.

A: What are you doing? Are
you doing your
homework at the
moment?

B: Don't be [5] ....· It's
Saturday morning! I'm
listening to my new CD in
[6] ....· What are
you doing?

A: I'm writing a story. I'm
[7] .... at stories!

Score ___ /6

Check your score

TOTAL ___ /40

Brilliant! (30–40)
Good! (20–29)
OK (10–19)

Score ___ /5

36 She works abroad.

Jobs

1 Rearrange the letters to make the jobs.

1 _dentist_ ....

2 ....

3 ....

4 ....

5 ....

2 Complete the crossword with jobs to match the pictures.

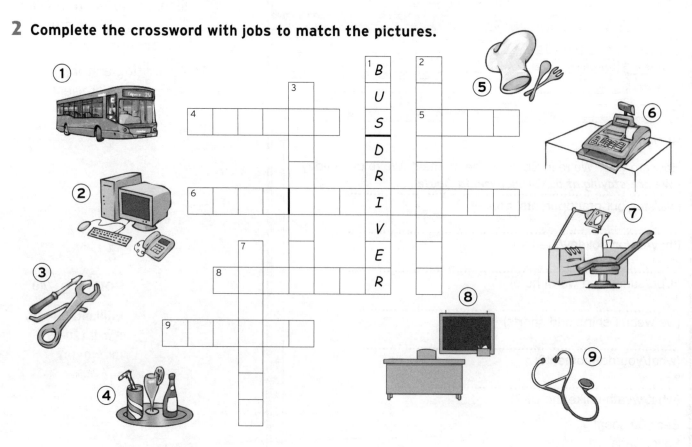

Places of work

3 Match the jobs and places of work.

1 shop assistant   a) office

2 nurse   b) restaurant

3 mechanic   c) hotel

4 receptionist   d) garage

5 secretary   e) hospital

6 chef   f) supermarket

1	*f*		2			3	
4			5			6	

What people do

4 Write about what the people in Exercise 3 do at work.

> repair cars   type letters
> ~~serve customers~~   cook food
> look after people   work

1   *Shop assistants serve customers in supermarkets.*

2 ....

3 ....

4 ....

5 ....

6 ....

Present simple and Present continuous

5 Match a sentence from A and a sentence from B to each picture.

A	B
He's a shop assistant.	He's teaching Italian.
He's a waiter.	~~He's repairing a car.~~
~~He's a mechanic.~~	He's working in a supermarket.
He's a doctor.	He's looking after a patient.
He's a teacher.	He's serving a customer.

1   *He's a mechanic. He's repairing a car.*

2 ....
....

3 ....
....

4 ....
....

5 ....
....

6 Complete the conversation with the correct form of the verb.

Sam: My dad [1] *'s* (be) a chef. What [2] .... (your dad/do)?

Amy: He [3] .... (be) a nurse.

Sam: That [4] .... (be) interesting! Where [5] .... (he/work)?

Amy: He [6] .... (work) at different hospitals. At the moment he [7] ....
(work) at Greenbrook Hospital.

Sam: [8] .... (your mum/work)?

Amy: Yes, she [9] .... · She [10] .... (be) a shop assistant. But she [11] ....
(not work) this week. She [12] .... (have) a holiday.

37 When's your birthday?

Ordinal numbers

1 Write the ordinal numbers.

1 *first* .... 12 ....
2 .... 13 ....
3 .... 17 ....
4 .... 20 ....
5 .... 21 ....
8 .... 30 ....
9 ....

**2 Write the letters of the alphabet.
Find the secret word.**

the sixth letter: *F*.....
the eighteenth letter: ....
the ninth letter: ....
the fifth letter: ....
the fourteenth letter: ....
the fourth letter: ....
the nineteenth letter: ....

The secret word is ....

Months of the year

3 Write the correct month.

1 It's the month after February and before April.
March..............................

2 It's the twelfth month of the year.

....

3 It's the eighth month of the year.

....

4 It's the month after May and before July.

....

5 It's the month after January and before
March.

....

6 It's the eleventh month of the year.

....

in/on

4 Complete the sentences with *in* or *on*.

1 My birthday's *in* March.

2 School starts .... September 5th.

3 School finishes .... July.

4 The concert is .... October 14th.

5 We always have a party ....
December 31st.

6 Do you always go on holiday ....
August?

Dates

**5 Write the birthdays of these famous
people.**

MAY
10th Bono
28th Kylie Minogue

JUNE
4th Angelina Jolie
20th Nicole Kidman

JULY
3rd Tom Cruise
26th Sandra Bullock

1 Bono's *birthday is on May 10th*.

2 Kylie Minogue's ....

3 Angelina Jolie's ....

4 Nicole Kidman's ....

5 Tom Cruise's ....

6 Sandra Bullock's ....

6 Read the sentences. Answer the questions.

- Amy's birthday is on the eleventh day of the fourth month.
- Hannah's birthday is ten days before Amy's birthday.
- Sam's birthday is on the fifth day of the eighth month.
- Elliot's birthday is twenty days after Sam's birthday.
- Jess's birthday is on the second day of the ninth month.
- Rusty's birthday is three days before Jess's birthday.

1 When's Amy's birthday? _It's on April 11th._

2 When's Hannah's birthday? ....

3 When's Sam's birthday? ....

4 When's Elliot's birthday? ....

5 When's Jess's birthday? ....

6 When's Rusty's birthday? ....

7 Complete the conversation.

> When's   get   It's   luck   on
> ~~How~~   date   in

Jess: Hi, Elliot. [1] _How_ are you?

Elliot: Fine, thanks. What's the [2] .... today?

Jess: [3] .... July 5th.

Elliot: [4] .... your birthday?

Jess: It's [5] .... September 2nd.

Elliot: Really? My birthday is [6] .... August. It's on August 25th.

Jess: So you're only twelve and I'm thirteen. Bad [7] ....

Elliot: That's OK. I [8] .... my birthday presents next month!

Listening

8 🎧16 **Listen. Complete the conversation.**

> No, tell me the month.
> Now look at the five cards in the magazine.
> That's amazing!
> What do you mean?
> ~~What's it about?~~

Rob: There's a good trick in this magazine.

Eric: [1] _What's it about?_

Rob: Birthdays. When's your birthday?

Eric: Guess!

Rob: [2] ....

Eric: It's in June. It's on ...

Rob: No, no. Don't tell me the day. Think of the number of the day.

Eric: [3] ....

Rob: If your birthday is on June 12th, the number is 12, but don't tell me the number.

Eric: I see.

Rob: [4] .... Which cards have got your birthday number?

Eric: Cards 2, 3 and 4.

Rob: Your birthday is on June 14th.

Eric: [5] ....

75

38 I want to buy a map.

Places in town

1a Rearrange the letters and complete the crossword. Find the secret word.

1 rca rapk

2 miiswgnm lopo

3 tensenawg

4 kusterreamp

5 pumretoc hspo

6 oasntit

	¹C	A	R	P	A	R	K	
2								
	3							
4								
5								
6								

The secret word is ....

1b Where can you buy these things?

1 a magazine? *a newsagent* ....

2 a hamster? ....

3 a cup of hot chocolate? ....

4 a train ticket? ....

5 a CD? ....

6 computer disks? ....

opposite/next to/in front of

2a Look at the map. What's the place?

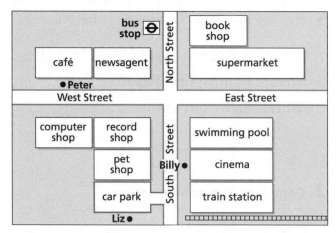

1 It's in South Street, next to the pet shop and opposite the swimming pool.
   the record shop
   ....

2 It's in East Street opposite the supermarket.
   ....

3 It's in West Street next to the café.
   ....

4 It's in South Street opposite the train station.
   ....

5 It's in North Street next to the supermarket.
   ....

6 It's in West Street opposite the computer shop.
   ....

2b Look at the map again. Complete the sentences.

1 The swimming pool is *opposite* the record shop.

2 The train station is .... the car park and .... the cinema.

3 Liz is .... the car park.

4 Billy is .... the cinema.

5 The pet shop is .... the cinema and .... the car park.

6 Peter is .... the café.

76

2c Complete the conversations.

1 **A:** Excuse me, where's the train station?

   B: It's _in South Street_, next to
the cinema and opposite _the car park_ .

2 **A:** _Excuse me, where's the supermarket?_

   B: It's in East Street, opposite the
swimming pool and next to the book
shop.

3 **A:** Excuse me, where's the car park?

   B: It's ...., next to
.... and opposite
....

4 **A:** ....

   B: It's in West Street, next to the computer
shop and opposite the newsagent.

5 **A:** Excuse me, where's the book shop?

   B: It's ...., next to
.... and opposite
....

6 **A:** ....

   B: It's in West Street, next to the
newsagent and opposite the computer
shop.

Let's ..., I want to ...

3a Circle the correct words.

Debbie: Hey, Joe. I'm ¹(hungry)/ _tired._
Let's ² _go_ / _going_ to a café and have
lunch.

Joe: Sorry, I ³ _can_ / _can't_, I haven't got
any money.

Debbie: It's OK. I've got ⁴ _any_ / _some_ money.

Joe: OK, thanks. After lunch, ⁵ _let's_ / _we_
go to the computer shop.

Debbie: Good idea. ⁶ _Let's_ / _I_ want to play
some computer games.

Mother: Joe! Lunch!

Joe: But Mum! I want ⁷ _to_ / _on_ go to
the café with Debbie.

Mother: ⁸ _Sorry_ / _Good idea_, you can't.
Your lunch is on the table.

3b Write the conversations.

1 **A:** _Let's go to a café._
I want to have a
drink.

   B: _OK. Good idea._ (✓)

2 **A:** _Let's go to a_
computer shop. I
want to play some
computer games.

   B: _Sorry, I can't._
I'm busy. (✗)

3 **A:** ....
....
....
....

   B: ....
.... (✗)

4 **A:** ....
....
....
....

   B: ....
.... (✓)

5 **A:** ....
....
....
....

   B: ....
.... (✗)

6 **A:** ....
....
....
....

   B: ....
.... (✓)

Reading

1 Match the photos to the texts.

New words
celebrate
poetry
meal
bagpipe
bring
parade
firework
burn

1 BURNS NIGHT

Burns Night is on January 25th. On Burns Night, Scottish people celebrate the life of their national poet, Robert Burns. They read his poetry and dance to traditional music. They also eat haggis, a traditional Scottish meal. A man always plays music on the bagpipes when they bring the haggis to the table.

2 INDEPENDENCE DAY

Independence Day is an important American festival. On July 4th, Americans remember their history, and they celebrate their independence from Britain. In the USA there are big parades in the streets and at night there are fireworks. Americans eat a lot of hamburgers on Independence Day.

3 BONFIRE NIGHT

Bonfire Night is a British festival. It's on November 5th. British people have bonfires in gardens and parks and they all watch fireworks. They burn a figure of a man (a 'guy') on the bonfires. They eat hot food, like soup, sausages and hot potatoes.

2 Complete the chart.

Name of festival	Country	Date	Activities	Food
Burns Night	Scotland		poetry, dancing	
Independence Day				
Bonfire Night			bonfires, fireworks	

3 🎧 **17** **Listen to Lara talking about a festival in her country. Complete the chart.**

Name of festival:	Saint Patrick's Day (the national saint of ....)
Date:	....
Countries:	...................../..................
Activities:	parades, traditional ....
Food:	........................./Guinness (a type of .... beer)
Traditional colour:	....

Writing

Portfolio

STUDY TIP!

We write: *October 31st* or *31st October*, but we say: *October the thirty-first* or *the thirty-first of October.*

4 Complete the chart.

June 22nd	1 *the twenty-second of June*
2	the eighteenth of October
February 20th	3 ....
4	the first of August
December 23rd	5 ....
6	the fifth of October
May 29th	7 ....

5 Write about St Patrick's Day in your notebook.

Saint Patrick's Day is an important festival ...

Cartoon Time: Future World

6 Complete the conversation. Use the words in the box.

Guess   idea   ~~trick~~   Here   luck   there

Ⓐ
Zar: Let's play a ¹ *trick* on Mixi.
Robomo: Good ² ....
Zar: Where are the eggs?
Robomo: They're over ³ ....

Ⓑ
Zar: Hi , Mixi. I've got a present for you. ⁴ .... you are.
Mixi: Wow! Thanks. What is it?
Zar: ⁵ ....!

Ⓒ
Mixi: Is it some eggs?
Robomo: Bad ⁶ ...., Zar.

1 Find the stickers. Write the name of the job.

1 He works in a garage. He repairs cars. He's a _mechanic..:_

2 She works in a school. She teaches students. She's a ....

3 He works in a supermarket. He serves customers. He's a ....

4 She works on a bus. She drives a bus. She's a ....

5 He works in an office. He types letters. He's a ....

6 She works in a restaurant kitchen. She cooks food. She's a ....

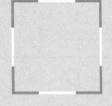

Score ____ /10

2 Write the correct form of the verb.

Billy: What does your father do?

Paula: He's a dentist. He [1] _looks after_ (look after) people's teeth.

Billy: Where is he today?

Paula: He [2] _'s shopping_ (shop) in town. He wants to buy a new tennis racket.

Billy: [3] .... he .... (play) tennis every week?

Paula: Yes. He [4] .... (play) tennis on Thursday evenings.

Billy: My mother [5] .... (teach) art on Thursday evenings. She's good at art.

Paula: What [6] .... she .... (do) at the moment?

Billy: She [7] .... (look after) my baby sister.

Score ____ /5

3 Rewrite the dates as we say or write them.

1 3/6 _June the third_ ....

2 15/9 _September 15th_ ....

3 14/4 ....

4 1/2 ....

5 29/12 ....

6 2/1 ....

7 20/10 ....

Score ____ /5

4 Complete the text about places in town.

The [1] 📖 book shop is opposite the [2] 🐱 pet shop.

The [3] ☕ .... is next to the [4] 🐱 .... and the newsagent. The [5] 🚌 .... is opposite the computer shop. The [6] 💿 .... is next to the computer shop. The [7] 🎫 .... is next to the [8] 💿 .... and the book shop.

Score ___ /6

5 Read the text in Exercise 4 again. Complete the map.

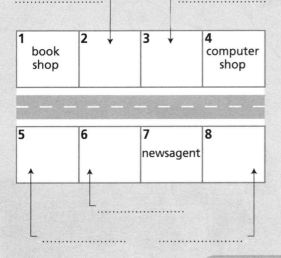

Score ___ /5

6 Rearrange the words to make sentences.

1 cinema go Let's the film see a to and

Let's go to the cinema and see a film.

2 shop Let's to buy a record CD go a and

....

3 busy Sorry, I'm can't, I

....

4 want play I games some to computer

....

5 some supermarket food a go to Let's buy and

....

....

6 a I to drink have want

....

Score ___ /5

7 Complete the conversation with the words in the box.

idea ~~Guess~~ luck joke there

Liz: Where's my camera?

Peter: [1] Guess ....

Liz: Don't be silly, Peter. Is it in your bag?

Peter: No, it isn't. Bad [2] ....!

Paula: Look, Liz. It's over [3] ....

Liz: Thanks, Paula. Come on, let's leave your brother alone.

Paula: Good [4] ....!

Peter: Hey, don't go. It's only a [5] ....!

Score ___ /4

TOTAL ___ /40

Check your score

Brilliant! (30–40)
Good! (20–29)
OK (10–19)

Go to page 88 to see Puzzle Story 4 and to page 92 for the play.

Puzzle Story 1

James Blonde in ...
'The brown Italian bag'

Miss Money-Honey: Look, James! What's that?

James: What, Miss Money-Honey? What?

Miss Money-Honey: Over there. Is it a bag?

James: Yes, Miss Money-Honey, it is. It's a brown Italian bag.

Miss Money-Honey: And who are they, James?

James: I don't know, Miss Money-Honey. It's a man and a woman. And they're not very friendly.

Miss Money-Honey: Interesting!

James: Yes, very interesting.

This is James Blonde and this is Miss Money-Honey. They're British and they're from London. James is very clever and Miss Money-Honey is his friend.

This is Clive Moss. He's thirty-eight years old and he's from Canberra in Australia. And this is Jill Marsh. She's forty-two years old and she's from New York in America. And what's in the brown Italian bag? Two books, a mobile phone and money! They are French books, a German mobile phone and British money. But is it his bag or is it her bag? This is a problem for James Blonde and Miss Money-Honey.

Clive: That's my bag!

Jill: No, it isn't. It's *my* bag, and *my* mobile phone and *my* money!

Clive: No, it isn't. It's *my* money!

James: Good afternoon. My name's Blonde, James Blonde. What's the problem?

Clive: This is *my* bag, not her bag. And it's *my* money.

Jill: No, it isn't. It's *my* bag and *my* money.

James: Hmm, one bag and two people. Miss Money-Honey, is it his bag or is it her bag?

Miss Money-Honey: I don't know, James. It's a problem.

> James Blonde and Miss Money-Honey are very clever but are you? Is it his bag or her bag?

James: What's your name?

Clive: My name's Clive Moss.

James: And what's your name?

Jill: My name's Jill Marsh.

James: Where are you from, Mr Moss?

Clive: I'm from Australia.

James: Where are you from, Mrs Marsh?

Jill: I'm not Mrs Marsh, I'm Miss Marsh. And I'm from New York. It's the capital of the USA.

James: And is this your mobile phone, Mr Moss?

Clive: Yes, it is. And those are my books and that's my money.

James: And who is 'SM', Mr Moss?

Clive: 'SM' is my wife, Sue Moss. It's her bag.

James: And are these your books, Miss Marsh?

Jill: Yes, they are. And that's my mobile phone and that's my money.

James: And who is 'SM', Miss Marsh?

Jill: 'SM' is my husband, Simon Marsh.

James: Hmm, very interesting.

New word
• problem

1 Read the information and answer the questions.

1 Where are James and Miss Money-Honey from?
They're from London.
....

2 How old is Clive Moss?
....

3 Is it 'Mrs Marsh' or 'Miss Marsh'?
....

4 Where is Clive from and where is Jill from?
....

5 Who is 'SM'? Complete the sentences.
Clive: 'SM' is my ....
Jill: 'SM' is my ....

2 Now solve the puzzle. Whose bag is it?

Is it: a) his bag?   b) her bag?

Puzzle Story 2

James Blonde in ...
'Where's the film star's diamond?'

James Blonde's house is in Oxford Street in London. Miss Money-Honey is James's neighbour. It's half past nine in the morning and they are in James's sitting room. It's a very nice sitting room with a big sofa and two armchairs.

Miss Money-Honey: I'm bored, James. Have you got a television?

James: No, Miss Money-Honey, I haven't. But I've got some books. Television is boring but books are interesting.

Miss Money-Honey: No, thanks, James. There aren't any pictures in your books.

James: You're hopeless, Miss Money-Honey!

Miss Money-Honey: It's only a joke! Look, James! Who's that at your window?

The woman at the window is Julia Foberts. She's a famous film star and she lives in London. She's tall and she's got long wavy hair. She's very beautiful.

James: Hello. Please come in. My name's Blonde, James Blonde. And this is Miss Money-Honey.

Julia: Thank you. My name's Julia Foberts.

Miss Money-Honey: Wow! Julia Foberts! Can I have your autograph?

James: What's the problem, Miss Foberts?

Julia: I've got a big problem, Mr Blonde. A thief has got my beautiful diamond. This is a photograph of the thief and this is a letter from the thief.

Dear Julia
I've got your beautiful diamond at my house in Scotland. Give me £1,000,000. No money, no diamond!

Love
Mr X

James: Hmm, very interesting! It's OK, Miss Foberts. This is a problem for Blonde, James Blonde.

Julia: Thank you, James. And thank you, Miss Money-Honey.

It's two o'clock in the afternoon. James Blonde and Miss Money-Honey are at the police station.

James: Look at the photo, Miss Money-Honey. What's interesting about the photo?

Miss Money-Honey: I don't know, James. What's interesting?

James: What's that in the photo?

Miss Money-Honey: Is it … the Eiffel Tower?

James: Yes, it is. So Mr X isn't in Scotland. He's in Paris, the capital of France. Inspector Smith, who are the famous French diamond thieves?

Inspector Smith: There are three: Pierre Bertrand, Michel Adjani and Philippe Forlan. Here are the police reports for Pierre, Michel and Philippe.

Police report 1

Pierre Bertrand is forty-six years old. He's tall and he's got dark brown eyes. He's got medium length dark hair. His flat is in Paris.

Police report 2

Michel Adjani is forty-three years old. He's tall and he's got medium length fair hair and dark brown eyes. His flat is in Paris.

Police report 3

Philippe Forlan is forty-five years old. He's got medium length fair hair and he's tall. He's got dark brown eyes. His terraced house is in Paris.

New words
- diamond
- police reports
- thief/thieves
- police station

1 Read the information and answer the questions.

1 Where is James's house? *James's house is in Oxford Street in London.*

2 Who has got Julia Fobert's diamond? ....

3 What's interesting about the photo? ....

4 Where is the thief? ....

5 Look at the photo. Is the thief in a house or flat? ....

2 Now solve the puzzle. Who is the diamond thief?

Is the diamond thief: a) Pierre?   b) Michel?   c) Philippe?

Puzzle Story 3

James Blonde in ...

'Who's got the gold?'

It's quarter to one on Wednesday afternoon and James Blonde is in a café with Miss Money-Honey. On Wednesdays, James gets up at half past six and plays the piano for an hour.
Then he has breakfast. After breakfast, he plays tennis with his friends. He has lunch with Miss Money-Honey at half past twelve.

Miss Money-Honey: What's that in your bag, James?

James: It's a tennis racket. I can play tennis very well. Can you play tennis?

Miss Money-Honey: Yes, I can.

James: And can you play the piano? I can. And I can play chess and I can play the guitar and ...

Miss Money-Honey: Oh James, please! Sit down and don't be silly!

James: Sorry, Miss Money-Honey.

After lunch James and Miss Money-Honey go to the bank but there's a problem at the bank. Inspector Smith is in the bank.

Miss Money-Honey: Look, James. There's a policeman. Why's there a policeman in the bank?

James: Excuse me, my name's Blonde, James Blonde. What's the problem? Can I help?

Inspector Smith: It's the bank vault, Mr Blonde. The gold isn't there. A thief has got all the bank's gold.

Miss Money-Honey: Oh no! Who is the thief?

Inspector Smith: We don't know. Mr Blonde, can you help us?

James: It's OK, Inspector Smith. I can help.

Inspector Smith: Great. Thank you, Mr Blonde. Here are some photos of the thief. Look at the time on the photos. It's lunchtime today!

James: Hmm, very interesting. Who has got keys to the bank vault?

Inspector Smith: Three people in the bank have got keys: Mrs Foster, Mr Potter and Miss Kane.

James: Where are they?

Inspector Smith: They're over there.

James: Good afternoon. My name's Blonde, James Blonde. Can I ask you some questions?

Mrs Foster: Yes, but I'm not the thief.

James: Can you drive, Mrs Foster?

Mrs Foster: Yes, I can, but I haven't got a car. Mr Potter can drive.

James: And Miss Kane? Can she drive?

Mrs Foster: No, she can't and she hasn't got a car.

James: Mr Potter, have you got a black T-shirt?

Mr Potter: No, I haven't. I've got a white T-shirt but I haven't got a black T-shirt.

James: Miss Kane, have you got a black T-shirt or baseball cap?

Miss Kane: No, I haven't, but I've got some beautiful dresses. Mr Potter and Mrs Foster have got black baseball caps.

James: Can I see your baseball caps?

Mrs Foster: Yes, my cap is in my car.

Mr Potter: No, I'm sorry, you can't. My son has got my baseball cap. He's in Spain.

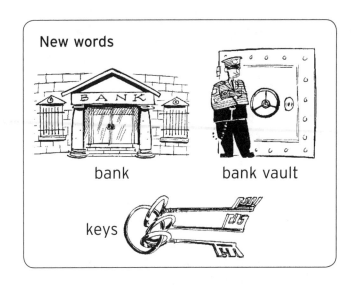

New words

bank   bank vault

keys

1 Read the information and answer the questions.

1   What time does James get up on Wednesdays?
    He gets up at half past six.

2   What can James do?

3   Where is the policeman? Why is he there?

4   Can the thief drive?

5   Who has got keys for the bank vault?

6   Who can drive a car?

7   Who has got a black baseball cap?

8   Where is Mrs Foster's baseball cap?

2 Now solve the puzzle. Who is the thief?

Is the thief:

a) Mrs Foster?   b) Mr Potter?   c) Miss Kane?

Puzzle Story 4

James Blonde in ...
'Which painting is real?'

It's ten o'clock on Saturday morning and James Blonde is washing his new red bike. It's warm and sunny and James is listening to the radio. James doesn't usually work on Saturday. He usually meets his friend Miss Money-Honey on Saturday and sometimes they cycle to the coast. But today, Miss Money-Honey is having lunch with Lord Tate. James's mobile phone is in his jeans. It's ringing.

James: Hello, three, six, nine, double oh, seven?

Miss Money-Honey: Hello, James. It's Miss Money-Honey.

James: Hello, Miss Money-Honey. Where are you?

Miss Money-Honey: I'm having lunch with Lord Tate. We're looking at his beautiful paintings.

James: Great. Are you having fun?

Miss Money-Honey: Yes, it's great. But James, there's a problem. Can you come to Lord Tate's house?

James: Sure. Let's meet there in thirty minutes. Lord Tate's got a new painting by Pablo Piccolo and I want to see it.

It's half past ten and James is at Lord Tate's house with Miss Money-Honey. They are talking to Lord Tate and Miss Stevens. Miss Stevens is Lord Tate's neighbour. There's a big problem. Lord Tate has a painting by Pablo Piccolo. The name of the painting is *The Spanish Coast in July*. But Miss Stevens also has a painting by Pablo Piccolo. The name of this painting is *The Spanish Coast in July* too. Which painting is the real one?

Miss Money-Honey: This is my friend. He can help you.

James: Good morning. My name's Blonde, James Blonde. What's the problem?

Lord Tate: This is my painting. It's *The Spanish Coast in July*. It's by Pablo Piccolo.

Miss Stevens: No, it's not. It's not the real painting. This is my painting and it's *The Spanish Coast in July* by Pablo Piccolo.

Lord Tate: No, it's not. *My* painting is the real painting!

Miss Money-Honey: These are the paintings, James. Painting 1 is Lord Tate's painting. Painting 2 is Miss Stevens's painting. Here's a book on Pablo Piccolo. Which painting is the real one?

James: Hmm, very interesting.

Miss Money-Honey: Can you help, James?

James: Don't worry, Miss Money-Honey. I can help.

Painting 1

Painting 2

The Spanish Coast in July is a new painting by Pablo Piccolo. Pablo is famous all over the world. In the painting, it is a hot sunny day. There are lots of people on the beach. They are all very happy but one person is very sad. She is sitting on a chair and she isn't talking to anyone. She's about fourteen years old and she's wearing a winter coat and sunglasses. Why is she sad? We don't know. Next to her is a family of five people, the parents and three children. One child is only two years old and he is eating a sandwich. Opposite the sad girl is a boy. He's about thirteen years old. He's listening to the radio and reading a book. His friend is next to him. She's a girl and she's playing a trick on him. She is putting a crab on his back. Behind the sad girl is a small dog. Is this her dog? We don't know but it's a beautiful painting.

New words

painting — crab

to ring

1 Read the information and answer the questions.

1   What is James doing at ten o'clock?
He's washing his bike.
....

2   Where is Miss Money-Honey?
....

3   Who is Pablo Piccolo?
....

4   Are both paintings by Pablo Piccolo?
....

5   In Painting 1, what is the boy reading?
....

6   In Painting 2, where is the dog?
....

2 Now solve the puzzle. Which is the real painting?

Is the real painting by Pablo Piccolo:

a) Painting 1?   b) Painting 2?

Venus and the Ice Cream

A play to act after Lesson 20

Characters

4 narrators
1 teacher
3 boys: Andy, Billy and Colin
3 girls: Delia, Emma and Fran
1 museum guard
1 announcer
2 statues: Caesar and Venus
Some extra schoolchildren

Narrators:

Ladies and gentlemen, our present for you,
Is a beautiful play, and everything's true!
The story is in the Bristol Museum.
Our actors are great, here you can see them!

In a room in the museum there are two statues standing on boxes. There is a big vase next to the statues. There is a guard in the room. The teacher and the children walk onto the stage. Delia is eating an ice cream. The others have bags.

Teacher: Hurry up, children! It's ten to five. We're late! Come on, come on!

Andy, Delia: Sorry, Mr Carson.

Teacher: Now, in this room, there are two interesting statues. They're 500 years old and very beautiful. Come and look.

New words
- museum • statue • vase • closed
- locked • broken

Emma: Mr Carson, I'm bored.

Guard: Sssh.

Billy: Me too, Mr Carson. Where's the museum shop?

Teacher: Don't be silly, please. It's five to five and we're late. Hurry up, children. Come on! Come on!

The teacher, extra schoolchildren and museum guard leave the stage. Colin takes out his camera. As he takes a photo, he breaks the vase.

Colin: I've got a camera. OK, everyone. Smile! [CRASH]

Boys and girls: Oh no!

Andy and Billy: The vase!

Fran: It's 500 years old and it's broken.

Announcer: Ladies and gentlemen, the museum is now closed. Good night.

Boys: The museum's closed.

Girls: The doors are locked.

Colin: Never mind. What about the windows?

Fran: Don't be silly. There aren't any windows.

Billy: What time is it?

Emma: It's two minutes past five.

Delia: Oh no!

The boys and girls sit down at the front of the stage. Behind the boys and girls, the statues begin moving slowly. As the boys and girls talk, the statues stand behind them.

Andy: Never mind. I've got some food. I've got an apple - well, half an apple.

Emma: Half an apple? Yuk!

Fran: I've got some oranges.

Colin: How many oranges have you got?

Fran: Two. But they're very old.

Colin: Old oranges! Yuk!

Delia: And I've got half an ice cream.

Caesar: What's an ice cream?

The boys and girls see the statues and scream. They run and hide.

Caesar: Venus, is this an ice cream?

Venus: I don't know, Caesar. Ooh! It's cold … and sweet. Have a taste.

Caesar: Mmmm. It's very strange! Is it a 'cream ice'?

Andy: No! It's an *ice cream*. It's a chocolate ice cream. But who are you?

Caesar: Who are *we*? Who are *you*?

Emma: We're from East Park School. We're on a school trip.

Venus: I'm Venus and this is Caesar.

Caesar: Welcome to our home.

Delia: Your home? But you haven't got a television …

Billy: Or a computer, or a stereo, or …

Fran: Sssh, Billy.

Venus: No, we haven't got those things. But we live here. This is our beautiful home and this is our beautiful vase … where's our beautiful vase?

Colin: Oh no! The vase. It's broken. I'm very sorry.

Venus: Never mind. It's only a vase. We've got some more vases. Come and look.

The statues and children go to the boxes. The statues take out lots of different vases.

Boys and girls: Wow!

Venus: This vase is 400 years old. It's very beautiful. This vase is 500 years old …

Fran: Great! It's an old vase − 500 years old.

Billy: Listen! It's Mr Carson.

Caesar: Who's Mr Carson?

Billy: He's our teacher.

Venus: Your teacher! Oh no! That's not good. Come on, Caesar. Hurry up!

The statues return to the same positions as before but Venus is still holding the ice cream. The teacher unlocks the door and comes in with the other children and the museum guard.

Teacher: Ah! You're here! The museum is closed. It's time to go home.

Andy: But Mr Carson, the statues, they …

Teacher: Yes, yes, yes. Now, hurry up! Come on! Come on!

Delia: But …

Teacher: Come on! Come on!

All the children leave the stage. Mr Carson is following them but sees the ice cream in the statue's hand. He goes and looks at it and scratches his head. Then he leaves the room. The narrators enter.

Narrators:

So boys and girls, ladies and gentlemen,

That's the end of our play. Is it ten out of ten?

Computer games are great, and music and pop stars,

But please remember this museum, these statues and that vase.

Freda's Fashion Show
A play to act after Lesson 40 🎧 23

Characters
4 reporters: Jim, Tim, Tracy and Stacy
2 fashion designers: Giorgio and Calvin
2 cleaners: Freda and Maggie
1 master of ceremonies (MC)
1 TV camera operator
4 models (2 male and 2 female)
Members of the audience

New words
- fashion designer • rich • cleaner
- expensive • cry • normal • sequin
- fashion show • reporter • catwalk

Tim: Look! It's Giorgio Arm-and-knee and Calvin Shine. They're the famous fashion designers!

Reporters: Giorgio! Calvin! Can we talk to you? Please!

Giorgio: Well, OK. But only for two minutes.

Jim: Yes, of course. Giorgio, you're very famous and very rich. Do you like your job?

Giorgio: Yes, I love it. I'm very good at my job and everyone loves me.

Tracy: And Calvin. What are your new clothes this year?

Calvin: Well, I always make beautiful clothes but this year my clothes are very, very beautiful. Look at this model. She's wearing a beautiful blue dress with a brilliant orange jumper.

Calvin clicks his fingers and Model 1 runs up to the reporters. She is wearing a horrible dress and a horrible jumper.

Stacy: Your clothes are very ... interesting. How much is the jumper?

Calvin: This jumper is £400 and this dress is £800.

Stacy: £800! That's very expensive.

Calvin: But my life is very expensive. I live in an expensive house, I eat in expensive restaurants and so my clothes are expensive.

Jim: And Giorgio, what are your new clothes this year?

Giorgio clicks his fingers and Model 2 runs up to the reporters. He is wearing horrible shorts, a horrible T-shirt and a baseball cap.

Giorgio: This model is wearing wicked grey shorts, they're £300, and a wicked ...

Calvin: Excuse me! It's quarter to three and the fashion show starts in fifteen minutes. Please sit down and wait for the fashion show.

Giorgio and Calvin leave, arguing. The reporters sit down. Maggie and Freda come onto stage. They are cleaning the catwalk floor. Maggie is wearing a Discman.

Freda: Maggie! Hey, Maggie! Can you hear me? MAGGIE!

Freda calls Maggie on her mobile phone.

Maggie: Hello? Three, five, six, double one?

Freda: Hello, Maggie, it's Freda.

Maggie: Hello, Maggie. Where are you?

Freda: I'm standing next to you!

Maggie: Oh, there you are. Sorry, Freda. I can't hear you. I'm listening to music on my Discman.

Freda: What music are you listening to?

Maggie: It's Mozart, Freda. It's very beautiful. I sometimes cry when I listen to it.

Freda: Maggie, do you like your job?

Maggie: Oh yes, I love it. I can talk to people, listen to music and I'm never bored. What about you?

Freda: I don't like my job. I want to be famous, very famous, and ...

Giorgio: Hey, the fashion show starts in two minutes. Hurry up!

Maggie: Don't be daft, Freda. Just be happy. Famous people aren't usually happy.

Freda: Really?

Maggie: Of course. They can't meet their friends. They can't go shopping. They can't have a drink in a café.

Maggie gives her Discman to Freda. They leave the stage, cleaning the floor. The audience come in and sit down.

MC: Ladies and gentlemen. Please welcome ... Giorgio and Calvin!

Giorgio and Calvin walk onto the catwalk. The music starts and Models 3 and 4 walk onto the catwalk. All the clothes are horrible.

MC: This is Daisy. She's wearing a beautiful dress. And this is Michael. He's wearing cool trousers and a beautiful shirt with sequins. The shirt is £500.

Tracy: Yuk! Those trousers are really ugly!

Stacy: Mmm, and those sequins are horrible!

MC: And this is ... er ... who is this?

Freda walks onto the stage. She is listening to her music and she doesn't know that she is on the catwalk. She starts to dance with her mop. The audience and reporters start to clap.

Freda: Hello? Eight, double four, two, three?

Maggie: It's Maggie. You're on the catwalk!

Freda: Where? Oh no!

Freda is very surprised but slowly she starts to enjoy the clapping. She dances more and everyone claps more.

Reporters: She's great! What's her name?

Maggie: Her name's Freda. She's my best friend!

Reporters: Freda, Freda, can we talk to you?

Calvin: Freda! Your clothes are cool! Do you want to work for me?

Giorgio: Freda, Freda. Come and work for me. You can be famous.

Freda: Can I be rich and famous?

Everyone: Yes!

Freda: Can I eat in expensive restaurants and live in expensive houses?

Everyone: Yes!

Freda: Can I go to the shops with my friends?

Everyone: Er, no.

Freda: Can I go to the park with my family?

Calvin: No, Freda, you can't. Famous people can't do normal things.

Freda: Oh! Well, I don't want to be famous. I don't want a new job. I want to be a cleaner with my friend Maggie. Come on, Maggie. Let's have a coffee in our favourite café.

Maggie: Good idea, Freda. Let's go.

Calvin: Yes, come on, Giorgio. Let's have a coffee too.

Giorgio: Good idea, Calvin. By the way, I like your shoes ...

Everyone follows Maggie and Freda off the stage.

Songs

🎧 02 Uncle Trevor and Auntie Kitty

(Lessons 1-5)

Here's a photo of my uncle,
And his name is Trevor Lee.
He is friendly and he is clever,
('Good morning, Tom') and
   he is forty-three.

Trevor, you're very clever,
You're so friendly too.
Clever Trevor is my uncle,
But my best friend is you.

Here's a photo of my auntie,
And her name is Kitty Dunn.
She is friendly and she is pretty,
('Hello, dear') and she is forty-one.

Kitty, you're very pretty,
You're so friendly too.
Pretty Kitty is my auntie,
But my best friend is you.

🎧 06 The Eight-Year-Old Rock Star

(Lessons 11-15)

I'm in my room, on my bed, there's a poster on my wall.
It's a poster of a great pop star and his name is Jon Paul.
Jon Paul's band is very cool, their songs are really great.
Jon Paul's band is the best in town, but Jon Paul's only eight!

Oh Jon Paul, oh eight-year-old Jon Paul,
Your band's name is *Rocking Gold*,
And you are very cool!

I'm in my room, the TV's on, there's a pop star on TV.
The pop star's from a famous band but his band's not for me.
The pop star's name is still Jon Paul, his band's still
   Rocking Gold,
But Jon Paul's band just isn't cool 'cos now he's nine years old.

Oh Jon Paul, oh nine-year-old Jon Paul,
You're not so great now you're not eight,
And your band's not so cool.

08 Where is Claire?

(Lessons 16-20)

I'm at the house,
Of my friend Claire,
And Claire has got
Long fair hair.
I knock, knock, knock,
But Claire's not there.
Oh, where is Claire,
With the long fair hair?

Claire's got a friend,
He's a big film star,
And the big film star
Has got a car.
I wait, wait, wait
For Claire and the star,
But they're very far
In the star's new car.

12 Stand Still and Don't Smile

(Lessons 21-25)

Can you stand still on your left leg?
Can you stand still on your right leg?
Can you hold your left foot with your right
    hand?
Can you keep a straight face and not smile?

Stand still and don't smile, stand still and don't smile,
Stand still and don't smile, now relax and stand up
    straight.

Can you touch your left knee with your right thumb?
Can you touch your right knee with your left thumb?
Can you touch both feet with both hands?
Can you keep a straight face and not smile?

Stand still and don't smile, stand still and don't smile,
Stand still and don't smile, now relax and stand up
    straight.

15 The Mouse Party

(Lessons 31-35)

Dad is in the kitchen, he's learning how to
    cook.
Mum is in the bedroom, she's reading a good
    book.
But when the house is empty, the mice begin
    to play,
They eat ice cream and watch TV and sing
    their songs all day.

Grandad's in the sitting room, he's playing
    cards with Jack.
Grandma's in the garden, she's having a big
    snack.

But when the house is empty, the mice begin
    again,
They drink milkshake, play music loud and
    turn it up to ten!

The dog is in the garden but the cat is in the
    house,
He's looking for a meal to eat, he's looking for
    a mouse.

When the cat is hungry, the mice all stay
    away,
They don't get up and don't sing songs and
    don't go out all day!

Pearson Education Limited
Edinburgh Gate
Harlow
Essex CM20 2JE
England
and Associated Companies throughout the world.

www.pearsonelt.com

First published 2009
Twelfth impression 2017

Set in 11.5pt Interstate Light
Printed in Malaysia (CTP-VVP)

ISBN 978-1-4082-0628-7 (Activity Book with Multi-Rom)

Acknowledgements

Illustrators:

Illustrated by: Katherine Baker (Sylvie Poggio), Adrian Barclay (Beehive Illustration), Kathy Baxendale, Humberto Blanco (Sylvie Poggio), Kate Charlesworth (Pennant Illustration), Peter Dennis (Linda Rogers Associates), Phil Garner (Beehive Illustration), Janos Jantner (Beehive Illustration), Sean Longcroft, Andy Robb (Beehive Illustration), Mark Ruffle (Sylvie Poggio), Theresa Tibbetts (Beehive Illustration), Sarah Warburton (Sylvie Poggio), Lorenzo Sabbatini

We are grateful to the following for permission to reproduce photographs:

Pearson Education Ltd: Gareth Boden 5 (tl); icponline 8 (t); Pearson Education Ltd: Gareth Boden 15 (tr); istockphoto: 18; Alamy: Rhinofilm: 19 (bl); icponline: 28 (t) (m); istockphoto: 28 (b); icponline: 38 (tr boy); istockphoto: 38 (tl); © Owen Price, (tl girl) © Eileen Hart, (ml) © Matthew Dixon, (ml boy) © Antonio Nunes, (tc) © Andrew Howe, (tc girl) © Elena Elisseeva, (bc), (bc girl) © Ana Abejon,(tr); Kathie Atkinson: 48 (l); icponline: 48 (tr); icponline: 70 (r);) © Steven Stone, 70 (tl); © Chris Schmidt, (bl)) © Chris Schmidt:78 (bl); ; icponline: 78 (bc) (tc), 78 (l),79

Alamy: Rhinofilm 27; icponline: 16, 23 (m), 38 (t) (m), 48 (tr boy), 60 (tr) (br), 70 (r), 82 (bc) (tc), 82 (l), 83, 92; istockphoto: 9, 26 (b), 38 (b), 48 (tl) © Owen Price, (tl girl) © Eileen Hart, (ml) © Matthew Dixon, (ml boy) © Antonio Nunes, (tc) © Andrew Howe, (tc girl) © Elena Elisseeva, (bc), (bc girl) © Ana Abejon, (tr) © Chris Schmidt, 49 (l) © Owen Price, (r) © Steven Stone, 70 (tl) © Chris Schmidt, (bl), 77, 81, 82 © Vasiliy Koval; OSF: Kathie Atkinson 60 (l); Pearson Education: Gareth Boden 21

Every effort has been made to trace the copyright holders and we apologise in advance for any unintentional omissions. We would be pleased to insert the appropriate acknowledgement in any subsequent edition of this publication.

Stickers

Lesson 5, Exercise 1

Lesson 23, Exercise 3a

Lesson 8, Exercise 3b

Lesson 26, Exercise 1b

Lesson 11, Exercise 1b

Lesson 32, Exercise 1b

Lesson 16, Exercise 1b

Lesson 40, Exercise 1